LOSING QUIN

Healing a Broken System
and a Broken Heart

. . . .

How one father's journey to find purpose after his son's death led
to the discovery of a secret epidemic in our healthcare system.

Brian Murphy

with contributions from Maria Galleher

D1040608

The Quin Murphy Foundation
www.quinmurphy.com

ISBN 978-0-692-08556-1

For Quin

Table of Contents

My Purpose
Looking to the Future to Redeem My Tragedy

"You must not hate those who do wrong or harmful things; but with compassion, you must do what you can to stop them, for they are harming themselves, as well as those who suffer from their actions."

- The Dalai Lama

When I found out my son's death was preventable, I was overcome with anger. I replayed the moments when doctors told me they thought Quin was exaggerating his pain, and that it was in his head. I wanted nothing more than to confront them with the full force of my rage. I was not the only one suffering; his death was an earth shattering event in our close-knit family. My Irish-Mexican family valued spending time together, so on every occasion after Quin's death, a simple meal became a constant reminder that one chair remained empty and our family was no longer complete. I was overcome with sadness, and sometimes the despair was so great, I prayed for God to take me. The pain was so intense, I could not bear it.

This despair would turn to rage that was difficult to tame, and

1

I worried it would alter me in a dangerous way. I loved Quin so deeply and devoutly, that I began to hear a faint voice that challenged my anger: *Why are you doing this? Are you doing this for the right reasons?*

I realized that my response to suffering had consequences. I could give my suffering a positive or a negative meaning. If I remained bitter, I would diminish Quin's life. On the other hand, if I allowed Quin's death to challenge me to explore my capacity to love and forgive, I could turn Quin's life into an affirmation of life.

I knew my path had to be one of compassion, but surely not mistaken for acceptance or weakness. When someone does great harm, the Dalai Lama said, "...one may need to take a strong countermeasure... to prevent harm to others… because there is a danger of that person's habituating in a very negative way."

In other words, compassion does not imply inaction. I realized that if I could help bring awareness to the medical system that took my son, and do it out of compassion instead of anger, I would be on the right path. I learned from reading *When Bad Things Happen to Good People*, that I had to change my question, from "Why did this happen to me?" to "Now that this has happened to me, what am I going to do about it?" I had to look to the future to redeem my tragedy. I found out that even small burdens are too difficult to bear if we feel they make no sense. On the other hand, nearly any pain or tragedy can be managed if we thought there was a reason or a purpose for it.

I had to find the purpose in all of this. I wanted nothing more than to honor Quin's memory, and, in telling his story, protect others from the same fate. I was influenced by writers like Harold Kushner and the Dalai Lama. Rabbi Kushner helped me to answer this question of myself: *Does my suffering serve good or evil, and where does it lead?*

Quin on a school trip with classmates and cousins in London, England.

I kept a journal during the last five months of Quin's life, after he became sick. I wrote down everything – Quin's symptoms, questions I had for doctors, and the answers they gave me. Quin's mother, Bo, and I worked as a team to navigate the complicated healthcare system. Bo and I met when we were young and she was my first serious girlfriend. We had two children together, Quin and Brianna. Unfortunately, it didn't work out between us, but we learned how to co-parent to be there for our children.

My story will begin at the end: the day I lost Quin. The following chapter comes from my journal entries, as I reflected on that day, six years later. Although I believe in accountability, I decided to change the names of the doctors to protect their privacy. I was influenced by the Institute of Medicine's report, *To Err is Human*, which states, "The majority of medical errors do not result from individual recklessness... Errors are caused by faulty systems... that lead people to make mistakes or fail to prevent them." So I tell this story not to shame good people who have erred; I tell this story to inspire systemic change that will protect patients, as well as healthcare providers.

The following chapter was the most difficult to write, but when I think about what Quin would have wanted, I imagine he would say to me, "Tell my story, Dad. Make things better."

Chapter One

Beginning at the End: The Day Quin Died

Journal Entry: January 27, 2010

3:00 a.m.: I have been by Quin's bed all night. He is in extreme pain. I adjust his favorite beanie on his head to keep his brown curls from falling into his eyes. I desperately try to help him find a more comfortable position to reduce his pain, but nothing works. He is suffering. Nurses come in to take his vital signs. Body temperature is the only reading they can get. Nurses cannot obtain a blood pressure reading from either arm, despite trying multiple times. A more experienced nurse comes in and tries to obtain blood pressure from Quin's ankles. No reading!

I can't think straight. *What is going on?! Why can't they get a reading?* I tell nurses Quin needs to be seen by a doctor. They tell me they are paging the doctor, and leave the room.

Quin's pain is unbearable. I am doing everything I can to make him comfortable. I ask him what his pain level is. He says, "Eleven out of 10, I'm hurting bad!"

The pain medication nurses administer is not helping anymore.

I ask nurses if there is something else they can give him. The doctor on-call prescribes Quin Morphine, but that doesn't help either.

4:00 a.m.: It's been an hour and the doctor has not responded to the nurses' pages. *Where is the doctor, why is he not here?* I'm panicking. "Quin! Hold on, the doctor will be here soon!" I tell the nurse, "Quin needs the doctor now!"

The nurse rushes out of Quin's room. I begin to see more activity; nurses coming and going. But no doctor. Quin is having a hard time breathing. I can barely hear his voice. It is difficult for him to move. Quin says to me, "Dad, I can't feel my legs or my arms."

What the hell is going on? Doctors have been telling us all along he was fine and we had nothing to worry about. All I can think is, *I'm losing my son!*

I can tell Quin is fighting to hang on. I tell him, "Please Quin, hold on, the doctor is on his way!"

Quin tells me, "Dad, I can't see. I'm seeing spots."

One of the nurses comes over and puts an oxygen mask over his face because he can no longer breathe on his own. Finally, Dr. Wren strolls in, seemingly unconcerned. I motion to the doctor, imploring him to hurry. As he approaches Quin's bed, I tell him, "He can't feel his arms or legs, and he's seeing spots. Do something!"

Dr. Wren responds, "I doubt he is seeing spots."

I look back at Quin and I see him pulling the oxygen mask from his face. I say,

"Quin, you can't take that off!" He leans forward and turns to the side as I hold him in my arms.

Quin begins to vomit. Black fluid gushes from his mouth. It just keeps coming out. It smells like death. I have never seen someone vomit so much, and I feel like I am in a scene from a horror movie.

I do everything I can to help Quin. I hold him in my arms and scream for help. Quin finally stops vomiting. I place him back on his bed. *Is it possible he is dead? He is not breathing!*

Nurses shout out, "Code Blue!" One nurse works quickly to free his breathing passage.

I turn toward Dr. Wren, pleading to him from my soul to save my son. I will this doctor to act quickly to stop this spiraling nightmare. Shockingly, instead of tending to my son, Dr. Wren backs away to the foot of Quin's bed.

I yell at him, "Why are you just standing there?! Do something! Do something!"

He stands motionless. He responds calmly, "We are."

I can't make sense of the situation and I think, *Why isn't he helping Quin? Why is he just standing there?*

4:30 a.m.: Chaos! Doctors and nurses hustle in and out of Quin's room, bringing extra equipment. The medical team surrounding his bed grows so much I can no longer see Quin. I stand on a chair, desperate to see my child's face. Watching the first urgent response from his caregivers, I fear it has come too late.

4:45 a.m.: I am on the tip of my toes, peering over the medical staff. I want so badly for Quin to look up at me. I want to see him take one more breath.

I feel like I am in a fire zone, but doctors and nurses don't seem to notice me as they run around me. I keep repeating in my mind, *Is this really happening?*

My mind refuses to believe what my eyes see. Then I snap back to reality, *I need to call someone.* I take out my phone and see the battery is almost dead. Without taking my eyes off of Quin, I call my wife, Laurie, and Quin's mother, Bo.

"Laurie, Quin is dying! He's dying!" I yell.

"No! It can't be, Brian," she responds, "Are you sure he is gone?"

"You have to come quick. Call Bo. My phone is dying," I say.

"Pray Brian, Pray hard!"

"I am... Dear God..."

Click. The battery on my phone dies.

5:00 a.m.: My family begins to arrive at the hospital. We gather in the hallway outside of Quin's room and quietly pray while we hold each other. I crouch on the floor and cover my head as my brothers and sisters hover over me. The sound of the double doors crashing open makes me look up. It is Bo.

Her voice is shaking. "Brian, what the hell is going on?"

My sister walks with her to Quin's room, where a young man is guarding the door. He holds his hand up and says, "You can't come in."

Bo responds, "I'm his mother! I don't care what you say, you can't stop me!"

He refuses. My sister pleads, "This is his mother! This might be the last time she sees her son! You guys really fucked up, the least you can do is let her see her son!"

A lone nurse walks out. She seems to ignore protocol and stands between the guard and Bo. She takes Bo by the hand and leads her into the room.

Seconds later, Bo runs out yelling, "He's dead! He's dead!"

She throws herself on the floor like a child in pain, kicking her legs, and pounding her fists on the floor.

My sister, Maria, cradles her and firmly says, "Bo, let's pray for a miracle. Pray with me that Quin will make it. It's not too late. It's not too late."

Bo takes a deep breath. Everyone is crying, and staff members arriving at work look around in shock. Everyone is shocked.

Chapter Two
The Third Leading Cause of Death

Imagine the reaction in our country if two jumbo jets crashed every day. When people die in large groups, there is a demand for immediate political action and systemic change. This is not the case for patients who die one at a time from medical errors.

In a 2014 U.S. Senate hearing before the Subcommittee on Primary Health and Aging, experts in the medical field testified that more than 1,000 people die every day due to medical error, costing the United States one trillion dollars per year. The cost of medical errors are vastly underestimated. They "...are costly in terms of loss of trust in the healthcare system... Health professionals pay with loss of morale and frustration at not being able to provide the best care possible... and society bears the cost of errors as well, in terms of lost worker productivity, reduced school attendance, and lower levels of population health status."

My 16-year-old son is part of this statistic. Quin died due to a series of medical errors, and missed and delayed diagnoses. According to the president of the National Patient Safety Foundation, Tejal Gandhi, M.D., delayed diagnosis is a significant issue related to medical errors.

If you think it can't happen to you, consider what the Institute of Medicine's report states: "Almost every American will experience an error in diagnosis in some point in their life."

In fact, medical errors are now considered the *third* leading cause of death in the United States. A Johns Hopkins medical study estimates that more than 250,000 patients die each year from medical errors. But this might be a conservative number. The studies authors say, "...no one knows the exact toll taken by medical errors... because the coding system used by the CDC to record death certificate data doesn't capture things like communication breakdowns, diagnostic errors and poor judgement..."

The study's authors claim that the inability to capture the full impact of medical errors results in a lack of public attention and a failure to invest in research that could address the problem. How is it possible that almost one in 10 deaths in the United States are due to medical error, and it is not front page news?

Johns Hopkins Patient Safety Expert, Dr. Peter Pronovost, was ranked fifth on the list of the 50 most influential physician executives in healthcare. He states:

> Why is it when a death happens one at a time, silently, it warrants less attention than when deaths happen in groups of 5 or 10? What these numbers say is that every day, a 747, two of them are crashing. Every two months, 9-11 is occurring... we would not tolerate that degree of preventable harm in any other forum.

In email correspondence with Dr. Pronovost, I thanked him for his visionary work in improving patient safety, and I asked him, "How does a common person like me help affect change?"

I was pleasantly surprised when he replied. His response was genuine and he was sorry for my loss of Quin. He said, "I know that love and not hate is the way we solve this… It is people like you sharing your stories in your local communities who will lead the charge."

That is why I want to be very clear: I am not questioning the integrity of doctors and nurses. People who go into the medical field are some of the brightest and hardest working individuals among us. If they are fortunate, they are hired into a comprehensive healthcare system that supports their best work, which results in fewer mistakes. Unfortunately, not all healthcare systems are equal, and almost none are truly comprehensive.

This is where my story begins.

Of the more than 250,000 deaths that occur each year from medical error, the death of one person in particular disrupted my life: my *only* son, Andrew Quinlan Murphy, who we called "Quin," died at the age of 16, due to a series of medical errors. On the day he died, I was told by doctors that things like this happen, and that even a relatively minor operation can sometimes lead to death. I was prepared to accept this explanation because I trusted and believed the experts.

When Quin died, a part of me died as well. I felt a gaping hole in my existence that could not be filled. I could have pushed on living this diminished existence, but a compulsion to know the truth drove me through this stage. I had to find answers on my own, because it did not make sense that a healthy teenager could die this way. My compulsion led me to spend countless hours doing research and finding experts who could guide me through Quin's medical records. I felt a bigger truth was hidden from me, a layperson, in the pages of his medical charts.

What I discovered is difficult for people to believe. Even healthy people with medical insurance are impacted by preventable errors. The kind of coverage one has makes a difference. Those who belong to a Health Maintenance Organization (HMO) are at a greater risk, according to Dr. Saul Seidman, author of *The Trillion Dollar Scam: Exploding Health Care Fraud.*

Dr. Seidman aptly describes an HMO as, "The six-minute appointment with a prescription." Short appointments with a quick "script" deliver copayments from the patients and further reimbursement from the HMO. This method of churning through patients is a profitable way to run a medical practice. In addition, there is a culture of secrecy that does not allow patients to make informed decisions. When buying a car, you can do research on the safest cars. As medical consumers, we don't have the same opportunity. Too often mistakes are covered up and protected by this policy of secrecy.

Counterintuitively, paying more for healthcare does not necessarily guarantee better outcomes. According to the Commonwealth Fund report, although the United States has the most expensive healthcare system in the world, "...[it] ranks last overall among 11 industrialized countries on measures of health system quality, efficiency, access to care, equity, and healthy lives."

Although the healthcare systems in Germany, the Netherlands, England, and Canada leave room for improvement, the United States healthcare system stands out for having the highest costs and lowest performance. For example, in 2011, the U.S. spent $8,508 per person on healthcare, while the United Kingdom, which ranked first overall, only spent $3,406.

A report from the Department of Health and Human Services expected healthcare expenditures to hit $3.35 trillion by 2016, which equates to an average of $10,345 for every U.S. citizen. This will lead to an increase in out-of-pocket costs paid by consumers. Maya MacGuineas, president of the bipartisan Committee for a Responsible Federal Budget, believes that government must have a plan to address these costs if it wants to demonstrate fiscal leadership.

How do the disparities in our healthcare system affect the individual? Unfortunately, now I know too well. In the United States, we can spend up to 17 times more than other countries for the same procedure, with little variation in quality. Our healthcare market is not transparent enough in its pricing. Therefore, we pay the highest premiums, but too often do not receive the best care. Quin was affected by this system. Not once did I think of cost or efficiency when I took Quin to his doctor's appointments. I assumed that by paying for health insurance, I would receive quality healthcare, but that was not the case.

As I struggled with my grief, I was comforted by the fact that people in my community were learning from Quin's story. I received calls and emails from friends and acquaintances asking for advice when they experienced medical roadblocks. They often thought of Quin's story and became stronger advocates for their own health. Although I was not able to save my son, my wish is that my experience can serve as guidance that might save others.

So how do I begin this story? After the loss of my son, the natural order of things was disrupted. Even now, years later, nothing seems normal, and there are days I barely have the strength to get up in the morning. Every day I struggle with the shock of seeing my only son die; reliving that moment over and over again. I wasn't given the opportunity to say goodbye because it was so unexpected. I was misled to believe my son would come home soon. My struggle seems eternal, with my faith and spirituality tested every minute.

After losing Quin, I was diagnosed with Post Traumatic Stress Disorder. And through the grief, I have experienced the opposite: post-traumatic growth. Humans are complicated and it's possible to suffer and grow at the same time.

I will attempt to explain the unexplainable. I believe my son's story must be told, because there is no doubt in my mind that this tragedy will be repeated needlessly unless we raise awareness and educate ourselves about healthcare advocacy. I understand that medical errors can never be fully eradicated, but I also know that they can be greatly diminished.

This story is not a simple repetition of painful memories or a recounting of my woes. That would only have a limited purpose and would not change the fact that my son is gone. I am not telling this story to elicit sympathy. My purpose is to tell a story of resilience and compassion, and to reframe the worst thing that ever happened to me into knowledge that can prevent further tragedies. Every human being has the power to reframe their story through positive action and compassion. It is possible to create a happy ending and to help others.

Chapter 3
Doctors Try to Explain

I waited outside of Quin's room with family. It was an agonizing three-hour wait. Finally, we were called into a private room where the team of doctors who tried to revive Quin met us. All 15 members of my family crammed in; my parents, my siblings, my wife, Bo, and her family. My identical twin brother, Conan, who knows my thoughts and actions even before I do, stood protectively behind me, with his hands on my shoulders. Laurie sat next to me with her arms wrapped around me.

A doctor, who I had not seen before, waited until we were settled. He paused for a second and said, "There is nothing more we can do."

Bo screamed, "You have to save him! I can't lose Quin! I can't lose Quin!"

Bo's oldest son, Chris, held her tightly, trying to restrain her raw and explosive emotions. Chris was only 2 years old when I met Bo, and I helped raise him. He wasn't my biological son, but I loved him like he was my own. He was now a young man in his 20s, trying to comfort his mom during the worst moment of her life.

The doctor said that even if they could resuscitate Quin, his brain had been denied oxygen for too long.

The words were so blunt. I felt my face tighten and my chest collapse. I remember thinking, *this must be what a heart attack feels like.* My twin brother immediately wrapped his arms around my chest and propped me up. He put his face so close to mine, I could feel his tears. He pleaded with me, "Please Brian, please don't give up. We need you to be okay. We can't do this without you."

Bo lost it. She was so angry that she started yelling at the doctors. She wanted them to bring Quin back. My dad was angry at the doctors, too. His jaw was clenched. Shaking his finger towards the team of doctors he said, "There is not a doctor among you!"

The doctor who delivered the news seemed taken aback by my dad's reaction. "What would you have had us do? We were the resuscitation team. We did all we could," he said.

My sister tried to calm the situation as she addressed the doctors. "I know you did the best you could, and we thank you," she said. "There has been no sense of urgency. For months we have been pleading for help, but no one seemed concerned. We knew something was wrong and no one listened. Where was the sense of urgency?"

They had no explanation. Standing apart from the group at the back, Dr. Wren was conspicuously silent. He would not look at us.

A nurse asked if we wanted to see Quin. I hesitated. I didn't know if I could see him like that. In that moment, I felt completely gone. I didn't know if I could handle one more blow. But I knew I had to see my son one last time.

Laurie held onto me as I walked in the room. I had tunnel vision and could only see Quin on the bed. I was unaware of anything else around me, but my sister said I made a deep guttural sound that filled the room. I tensed my muscles and clenched my fists like I wanted to hit someone. I walked over to him. I kissed him on the forehead and said, "I love you, Quin."

As I started to leave, I remembered something. I picked up Quin's beanie, and I clutched it against my chest as I left the room for the last time.

The medical examiner would arrive later, and tell my family that it is unusual for an active 16-year-old to die from an appendectomy, minor surgery performed one week earlier. She said the medical examiner's office would take possession of Quin's body and do a thorough autopsy to identify the cause of death.

My thoughts spun through the day's events, locking on the doctor's assurance that all would be well. Instead, I witnessed the last day of my son's life. It was impossible to believe that this nightmare began five months earlier, when Quin complained of a stomach ache. I remember when it all began.

Chapter Four
Misdiagnosis and Inappropriate Treatment From the Start

First Visit to the Emergency Room

The misdiagnosis, which resulted in consistently inappropriate treatment, started almost five months before Quin's death. I did not know at the time how common misdiagnoses and ineffective treatments are in the United States. In *Trillion Dollar Scam: Exploding Health Care Fraud*, Dr. Seidman explains how the scenario of misdiagnosis, and confused and inappropriate treatment is repeated thousands of times in our healthcare system. Too often, doctors do not have sufficient time to listen, ask questions, or observe. Diagnostic testing is very useful, but not to the exclusion of observing and interacting with the patient. Test results alone can lead to educated-guess diagnosis with consequences that are sometimes lethal. This is precisely how Quin's journey began and ended.

It was late summer, and we were on our way to soccer practice. Quin turned to me and said, "Dad, I'm having some stomach pain and it's not going away."

Even though he said the pain was getting worse, he still wanted to practice. He had never missed a practice and he was proud of this. I had an uneasy feeling; however, and I told him we needed to go to the emergency room as a precaution.

Quin took pride in his athletic ability and health. He was in excellent shape and the fastest player on his team. I knew that Quin was feeling lousy since he agreed to skip practice and go to the emergency room. When we arrived at the field, I quickly got out of the car and walked over to the coach to let him know Quin was not feeling well. Quin's coach was understanding and hoped that everything was okay.

We arrived at the emergency room of Kaiser Permanente, our HMO, and checked-in. The waiting room was filled wall-to-wall with people and we waited three-and-a-half hours to be called in. We were escorted into an exam room that looked more like a storage unit. I could only assume we were in that room because they didn't have enough space to accommodate everyone in exam rooms.

A young doctor walked in. Quin and I explained his symptoms; abdominal pain, problems urinating, and constipation. The doctor looked puzzled. I asked the doctor what he thought it was. He said he didn't know what it could be, and he didn't seem curious to find out. He suggested inserting a catheter to drain Quin's bladder.

Although Quin was complaining about constipation, abdominal pain, and urinary problems, the doctor only focused on one thing: the urinary issue. He did not address Quin's symptoms in their totality. I asked if this catheter would solve Quin's problem. He responded by saying, "I don't think so."

Puzzled by this response, I asked if we could have a second opinion. He said that he would get the pediatrician to take a look at Quin, but when he came back 15 minutes later, he said the pediatrician had no idea what could be causing the symptoms. I had a feeling he was just guessing. My confidence in the doctor diminished quickly. I asked him if I could talk to Quin privately. He nodded and left the room.

Quin and I agreed that this doctor did not have our full confidence and we didn't want him doing any procedure since he was unsure whether it would help. He could be doing more harm than good. I called the doctor back in and told him we were declining any procedure at this time and would be following up with Quin's primary care doctor. I signed the necessary forms and we went home.

My fear that Quin's doctors were not taking the time to analyze all of his symptoms was confirmed when I read Dr. Seidman's book. He details the problems facing our deteriorating healthcare system. He describes a patient who was misdiagnosed because doctors were focusing on small details instead of looking at the patient as a whole. This patient had swollen ankles and difficulty breathing, and his history included a major heart attack, followed by a kidney transplant. When the patient arrived at the hospital, the cardiologist did a series of tests and declared the patient was not having heart complications. After a chest X-ray, the cardiologist, a heart specialist by training, thought the patient had pneumonia and prescribed a sulfa drug to fight the lung infection.

To ensure the patient did not have heart failure, the cardiologist performed a trans-echocardiogram. The doctor did not find the test to be abnormal for heart failure, so the treatment for pneumonia continued. The patient received three liters of intravenous fluid per day, which his weakened heart and ailing kidneys were unable to tolerate. None of the specialists recognized the cause of the patient's continuing decline. There was no one in charge to coordinate the activities and decisions being made by all of the specialists. No one was in charge of the patient's treatment.

Eventually, the patient's brother, who was an experienced

cardiologist, flew in from out of town to be by his brother's bedside. He immediately made a clinical diagnosis of congestive heart failure. No tests were needed to make the diagnosis, and the patient improved as soon as the proper treatment was given.

Had the heart patient not had a brother who was a cardiologist, as most of us do not, he could have easily died. Dr. Seidman believes physicians are under a tremendous amount of pressure to see more patients in less time. Examining the patient and proceeding thoughtfully are critical when treating a patient. A doctor's medical knowledge is demeaned when they are pressured by insurance companies and HMOs. When specialists do not cooperate with one another, each doctor evaluates a part of the patient instead of the whole. Too often, doctors focus on their computer screens and test results at the expense of their patients, and the outcome can be disastrous.

In our case, almost every time Quin had an appointment, the doctors had their eyes on the computer screen rather than asking him questions. Like many parents who have lost a child, I have played the "what if" game. What if I had a doctor in my immediate family, like this patient who was saved? Every day I fantasize about a different outcome. What could I have done differently? The answer; however, is that we shouldn't have to have a doctor in our family to make sure our children are safe.

After Quin died, I obtained a copy of his medical records and my concern was confirmed. Doctors only focused on one small part of Quin's complications instead of looking at all of his symptoms and the broader implications.

Chapter Five

The Competitor is Benched

Three Months Before Quin Died

Quin's greatest passion was playing soccer. He would practice for hours on his own or with friends. He was fiercely competitive and hated to lose. His speed and quickness set him apart. By October, three months before he passed away, he was mostly watching from the sidelines. He was in too much pain to do what he loved most.

Watching from the bench was not something Quin ever did. He loved to compete. One year before he got sick, I remember a race he competed in, a one-mile run. There were some very fast runners competing that day, including people who belonged to a local track team. The only training Quin had was at soccer practice, so he had never focused on the one-mile run. I knew Quin was fast, but these top runners had been training. The coach for the other runners was there warming them up, preparing them for the race. I was nervous for Quin, but he didn't seem worried at all. Quin was so competitive he couldn't let anyone be in front of him, even if it was a friendly hike. I pulled him aside and told him he needed to pace himself and not worry about being in front for the entire race. I thought to myself, *There is no way he is going to be able to do that.* I said, "Hang back about the middle of the pack for most of the race." With a sideways glance he asked, "What?!"

"Just do it, Quin. It will work. Trust me. In the last quarter-mile, make your move and use that speed." He liked that part of my strategy.

I knew it was going to be hard for him to follow through with my suggestion. However, he agreed and trotted over to the starting line. There were 13 runners competing in the race. They all lined up. The signal was given and they were off. Quin was doing exactly what I had told him and he was hanging back. He was right in the middle, in about sixth or seventh place, halfway through the race. He was looking strong and not laboring at all, as if he were gliding. That is how he ran.

With about a quarter-mile left in the race, he made his move and darted in front of everyone leaving them behind. He was creating distance between him and the rest of the runners. I was so excited and jumping up in the air. I kept telling myself, "I can't believe it! I can't believe it!"

When he crossed the finish line, he was 50 yards ahead of the next runner. I ran over and gave him a big hug, "Wow, Quin! That was amazing!" The person in charge of keeping time on the runners came over and said to Quin, "Great race! Your time was 5 minutes 10 seconds."

The track coach made his way over to us and congratulated Quin, "You are fast, young man. Congratulations!" and handed me a flyer for his track team. "I would love for your son to come out and run with us."

I thanked him and he walked away. I knew Quin had potential as a runner. He was a natural. I asked him if he wanted to run track, but he had no interest. All he cared about was soccer.

Quin and I were very much alike. When Conan and I were in high school, we played varsity soccer, football, and baseball. A friend of ours, who was on the track team, asked us to participate in the mile-relay of a county invitational. They were in a bind because they didn't have enough runners. Conan and I weren't sure because we didn't consider ourselves runners, so we were a little worried. All we knew was that we wanted to win. We pushed ourselves so hard, we threw up at the end of the race, but we won.

One year after Quin ran that mile race, life started to change. Before his symptoms started, Quin was on the starting lineup of his soccer team and an important part of the team's success. He eventually stopped going to practice completely, although if he was feeling up to it on the weekends, he would attend the games. Despite not feeling well, Quin tried his best not to show his discomfort so he could get on the field, even though it would only be for a short time. I knew Quin wasn't 100 percent, but he was happiest when he was able to run around on the soccer field. It gave him some relief and took his mind off his pain. Since he didn't make practices, his coach limited his play time. His coach told me he could not justify keeping Quin on the starting lineup. I understood completely, and it was better that Quin limit his activity anyway. For most of the season, his team was fighting for first place, so every game was crucial.

Another thing that distracted Quin from his pain, was the love and support of his large family. My brothers and sisters lived nearby, and Quin grew up with all of his cousins. In October, we had planned a family trip to Disneyland. I was only planning to take my daughter, 8-year-old Brianna. She was so excited about going and asked if her big brother would join us.

"Dad, can Quin come? I have never been to Disneyland without him." I was almost sure Quin would not feel up to it, but I didn't want him to feel left out so I asked him if he wanted to come.

"I'm taking Brianna to Disneyland with all the cousins. What do you think? How do you feel?"

Before I could even finish my sentence, Quin responded, "For sure I want to go!"

I was surprised and really happy. All 10 cousins, ranging in age from 2 to 17, were there. We had many family pictures, but we didn't have one where all 10 were in the same shot. Quin's cousin Connor almost didn't make this trip. He was in his senior year of high school, taking six advanced placement classes, and had a lot of homework. He stayed home to study. A half-hour into our two-hour drive to Disneyland, Connor's mom, Maria, got emotional.

"What's wrong?" her husband, John, asked.

"All of the cousins are going to be there," she responded, "I really want Connor to come."

John immediately got on the phone and called Connor. "Get ready. We are driving back to pick you up."

That day we took the first and last picture that included Quin and all of his cousins.

Quin, 16 years old, with all of his cousins at Disneyland.

Chapter Six
Patient-Churning: Quin's Last Soccer Game

Two Months Before Quin Died

Despite an emergency room visit that had provided so few answers, I decided to take Quin to a family friend, a doctor in Tijuana, Mexico. Dr. Heberto Lopez had been treating our family for many years. Some people might question why I would take my child to a country that is considered less advanced in the medical field. Our family's experience; however, was only positive. In the United States, we were lucky to get five minutes with a doctor who didn't know us by name. In Mexico, our family doctor often spent more than an hour catching up and learning everything about us.

Plus, Dr. Lopez had saved my life when I was 9 years old. I had an extremely high fever, muscle aches, weakness, and abdominal pain, so my parents had taken me to our doctor in the United States. The doctor said it was probably the flu and that I would be fine after it ran its course. Unfortunately, my symptoms got worse and we had to return to the doctor. He told my parents that I was making up my symptoms, because I was not getting sufficient attention at home. My mother was furious and decided to take me to see Dr. Lopez.

I remember sitting in the office with my mother and Dr. Lopez. Even before the examination, we had a 20-minute conversation. He asked all kinds of questions about my daily routine, including my diet and exercise, my sleep routines, my school, and my friends. I thought it was odd at the time, but looking back I know now that was part of his examination. He gave me a physical exam and asked about my symptoms. At the end of the conversation, he told my mother, "I believe I know what it is, but I will draw blood just to make sure I'm right."

Typhoid fever. He was right. Left undiagnosed and untreated, typhoid can be fatal.

Now, it was Quin's turn to see Dr. Lopez. My mother, Rose Mary, came with us. She and my father had known Dr. Lopez for more than 30 years. His children had been in my father's karate class in Tijuana.

It had been several years since I last saw Dr. Lopez. He had a tiny office with several books on the shelf. It resembled an office you might see on television in the 1950s or '60s. I gave him a big hug and he was happy to see us. We sat down and Dr. Lopez began thoroughly and comprehensively examining Quin. For nearly half an hour, he asked questions about everyday life. After the physical examination and blood work on Quin, we scheduled another appointment for the following week. During that week, Quin's condition worsened. Painful urination and watery stools made it difficult for him to leave the house for an extended period of time, knowing he wouldn't have access to a bathroom.

His condition became so extreme that by the day of his follow-up appointment, Quin knew he could not be caught without access to a bathroom for the hour or two it could take to cross the border.

However, Quin was able to produce a urine sample, so I decided to take it to Dr. Lopez. Tests were inconclusive, but there was no detection of an infection. Given all of Quin's symptoms, Dr. Lopez said he believed Quin had celiac disease or some gastrointestinal issue related to an allergy to gluten. I had never heard of celiac disease. He took out one of his books and showed me. Celiac disease causes inflammation to the intestine, which can cause stomach pain, bloating, and diarrhea. He explained that it is common among people of Northern European descent, and is very prevalent with people from Ireland. My great-grandfather, Quin's namesake, was an Irish immigrant.

Since that encounter, I have read every study I could get my hands on to find more clues. I found out that celiac disease is much more prevalent than once thought. Dr. Alessio Fasano, one of the world's leading authorities on celiac disease, found that it was 40 times more common in the U.S. than once thought, estimating that one in 250 Americans suffer from it. Another expert, Benjamin Lebewohl, Director of Clinical Research for the Celiac Disease Center at Columbia University, found that celiac disease is not exclusive to people of Northern European or Irish decent. His studies have found celiac disease in virtually every country in the world.

Dr. Lopez was adamant that there was an intestinal issue that had to be addressed. He recommended a battery of tests to zero-in on a diagnosis. He said that he could get the tests done at a clinic in Tijuana, but suggested that we have them done in San Diego, through our local healthcare provider.

It was striking to me that Dr. Lopez made a diagnosis related to gastrointestinal issues in one week, while the doctor at Kaiser, could only guess that it was a urinary issue; a possibility that Dr. Lopez immediately dismissed.

We scheduled an appointment with a primary care physician

at Kaiser, Dr. Dobson. After a physical exam, a urinalysis revealed traces of blood in Quin's urine. Dr. Dobson determined that Quin probably had a urinary tract infection and prescribed antibiotics.

I noticed that Dr. Dobson's feet were always pointed towards the door. I didn't know what that meant, but it made me feel uneasy, like we were wasting her time. Now I know why she always seemed rushed. Dr. Seidman explains the profit-driven, patient-churning model practiced by most HMOs consists of "...new prescriptions, more tests, and more co-pays..." He claims that this fast-paced, for-profit model makes good patient care "...more of an accident than a determined event." In our case, this resulted in no clear diagnosis. Instead we got the six-minute appointment, followed by an expensive prescription.

While Dr. Dobson insisted Quin had a simple urinary tract infection and there was nothing serious to worry about, my son had dropped 15 pounds in 2 months. He was down from 125 pounds to 110 pounds. My instincts were telling me something was terribly wrong, yet the doctor smiled and shrugged. She didn't have time to connect the dots. Constipation and diarrhea (seemingly contradicting symptoms), abdominal pain, weakness, reduced energy, and loss of over 10 percent of his body weight. *Wasn't she at least curious?*

Later in the evening, after his appointment, Quin's pain spiked. I knew we had not given the antibiotics a chance to take effect, but the intensity of his pain alarmed me. He rarely complained, so when he did, I knew it was bad. I called and spoke to a screening nurse, explaining Quin's symptoms. She recommended taking Quin to the emergency room.

While we waited in the emergency room for a couple of hours, I could not help but recall our last experience. I hoped this visit would provide some clarity. This time, the doctor seemed attentive and compassionate about Quin's painful symptoms. Once again, his tests were inconclusive.

The doctor advised Quin to continue on the course of antibiotics to give it time to fully take effect. He was unable to explain Quin's abdominal pain and also did not detect any blood in Quin's urine, as Dr. Dobson had indicated at his earlier appointment. Again, the Kaiser doctors' primary focus was on Quin's urinary issues, and they continued to dismiss the abdominal pain. However, unlike his primary care physician, this doctor referred Quin to a urologist. I thought it was odd that Dr. Dobson had not made the same referral.

We made our way home, feeling discouraged once again. Quin's condition seemed to get worse by the day. Blood tests and urine samples did not determine a cause for Quin's ailments, and his weight loss didn't raise any red flags for doctors. It was as if they were confused and refused to look for possible solutions.

During this time, there was a TV series called *House*; a medical drama about a genius, Dr. Gregory House, who led a team of diagnosticians. He successfully identified patients' illnesses by observation, subtle insights, and team troubleshooting. I would watch this fictional drama, and crave the same attention to detail or even some curiosity about the oddness of Quin's pain. But the doctors only had a few minutes to spend with us, and there was no time for anything more than a prescription to mask the symptoms.

After four days of antibiotics, Quin's symptoms continued with no relief. Bo called Dr. Dobson to tell her that Quin was still in pain. Without seeing Quin again, Dr. Dobson changed the prescription to a different antibiotic, Trimethoprim-Sulfamethoxazole, hoping that would solve the problem and ease Quin's discomfort. My instinct again was that she was just guessing.

Throughout all of the appointments, Quin was still hoping that he would make a quick recovery and get back on the soccer field. His team made the playoffs and had a tournament an hour away in Irvine, California. He wanted to go, but that would depend on his test results.

Quin had the appointment with the urologist. The doctor performed a cystoscopy on Quin. A cystoscope is a thin tube with a camera and light on the end. This tube is inserted through the urethra and into the bladder, so the doctor can visualize the inside of the bladder to detect any abnormalities. This test was also inconclusive. As we left the Kaiser office, Quin said he was feeling fine and wanted to go to his soccer tournament. I remember thinking to myself that he wasn't fine, but he wanted me to believe he was better. His love for soccer was deep and it showed on the field when he played. I agreed, but told him it wouldn't be a good idea for him to play. It was a playoff series and he desperately wanted to help his team.

Saturday morning was the first game. He struggled in the bathroom for a while, but we made it to the field. I told the coach he wasn't feeling very well and he probably wouldn't be able to play. He sat next to me in a folding chair as the game began. The team was struggling and the other team scored a goal. The coach walked over to us and asked if Quin could play. Quin looked over at me and said, "Dad, I want to play."

I was scared for him, but maybe he was getting better. Doctors gave us no indication that it was anything severe. Still, I was reluctant. Quin was a fighter and never backed down from a challenge. He went into the game and I closely watched his every move. Quin was all over the field, running and chasing down the opposing team's best players. The momentum shifted back to our side and we tied the game.

After about 20 minutes, I noticed Quin slowing down. He had a look of agony on his face. He wanted to stay in, but I knew he was done. He refused to tell the coach to substitute him out. I ran over to the coach and told him to take Quin out right away, and he did. I went over and helped Quin to his chair as he flopped into it. He was noticeably exhausted and pale. I felt like I had made a horrible mistake by allowing him to play. With Quin out of the game, the momentum shifted back to the opposing team and they quickly regained the lead. The coach came over and asked if Quin was able to go back in. Even though Quin wanted to, I said, "No." At the end of the game the coach came over to us and said, "I wish I had more players on the team with the same passion and fight as Quin. We would have won the game."

The coach's comment made Quin feel good and I noticed that it boosted his spirit, but I wasn't going to let him play another game at that tournament.

How was I to know that would be the last game he'd ever play?

Chapter Seven

Quin Deteriorates: Doctors Don't Have the Time to Make a Proper Diagnosis

One Month Before Quin Died

In December, we made another appointment for Quin with his primary care physician. It had been two months since these symptoms sidelined him. He wasn't playing soccer and he couldn't go to school, because he couldn't leave the house for any length of time. Most shocking to me was that he weighed 110 pounds. In early September, he weighed 125 pounds. He always had a slim, athletic build, and he could not afford to lose even a pound. Quin was deteriorating right in front of me.

I was so desperate that I spent hours on the computer researching Quin's symptoms in anticipation of the doctor's appointment. I wanted to ask Dr. Dobson if Quin may have some intestinal disorder, as our doctor in Mexico suspected. I was also sure that when she saw how much weight he had lost, and that he couldn't attend school, she would respond more aggressively.

Patient advocates recommend that the best defense for your health care is self-education. That is what I was doing. I had gone to a different doctor for a second opinion. I read peer-reviewed medical studies, and I prepared to ask questions.

The day finally came. Quin's mother took him to the appointment and I left work early to meet them. When I arrived, Quin and Bo were already inside. I was escorted back. When I walked in, Dr. Dobson was already on her way out of the room. I couldn't believe it. She had only spent a few minutes with Quin. As she was walking out of the room, I tried to engage her in conversation. I desperately wanted my son to be well. I wanted her to listen just for a couple of minutes. She seemed unconcerned about Quin losing 15 pounds in two months. In desperation I continued, "Is there a possibility of Quin having an intestinal disorder, such as irritable bowel syndrome?"

She kept walking as she answered, "No, he doesn't have an intestinal disorder. Just go to the lab and get some blood drawn."

She seemed so sure. She was completely focused on Quin having a urinary tract infection. How could she be so certain? Every time I typed in a search engine on the computer a variation of Quin's symptoms, the search engine lead me to some type of an intestinal disorder. I had hoped that if I found the diagnosis, then we would be closer to a remedy. But Dr. Dobson's curt response felt like a punch in the stomach. I was confused. I trusted doctors. They knew more than me, so I had to believe them, right?

She could not explain all of Quin's symptoms; excruciating abdominal pain, loss of weight, nausea, chronic constipation, yet always feeling like he had to go the bathroom. He was unable to go to school or play soccer, but the doctor just ordered more tests and in addition to the antibiotics she prescribed, an antispasmodic medication. However, this did not help either. Nothing she was doing helped Quin at all.

Why couldn't they see what I could clearly see? In my mind, it was an emergency. But for the doctor, this did not even warrant a referral to a specialist.

The doctor-patient relationship is considered one of the most important components of good care, but the United States is dominated by a fee-for-service payment model that rewards doctors who see more patients. In a *PBS News Hour* article, the claim was made that it is common for a primary care physician's appointments to be scheduled at 15-minute, or even 11-minute, intervals, but rushed doctors listen less:

> A 1999 study of 29 family physician practices found that doctors let patients speak for only 23 seconds before redirecting them; only one in four patients got to finish their statement. A University of South Carolina study in 2001 found primary care patients were interrupted after 12 seconds...

Another expert, Dr. Tom O'Bryan, believes that knowing a patient's complete health history is essential. His checkups include a detailed timeline of a patient's health, "starting with your birth history, health in infancy, childhood, and young adult; vaccinations; fevers; antibiotic use... anything that has happened that may have contributed to the 'you' of today."

Not once did doctors at Kaiser ask about Quin's personal health history. There was simply no time to ask questions and less time to wait for a response. As a result, they were unable to determine a correct diagnosis. I found more accurate information using Google than I did speaking to the doctors. I barely had time to express my concerns, and when I did, they were summarily dismissed.

I was disappointed in what seemed like a lack of empathy, but kept on calling the helpline to report Quin getting worse. Finally, Dr. Dobson agreed to take a stool sample analysis. I felt hopeful that this would give us the answers we were seeking. It was extremely difficult to acquire a clean stool sample due to the consistency of his bowel movements, but Quin was finally able to give us a sample. When I saw what it looked like, I was dumbfounded. The liquidy stool had yellow bile, with sticky, stringy-looking pieces, and it emitted a foul odor. I was sure when the doctors saw this sample, they would realize something was terribly wrong.

Bo took it in to be analyzed. Before dropping it off at the lab, Bo decided to go by Dr. Dobson's office to show her the sample and express her alarm about the stool. She wanted to describe to the doctor what we had seen. Bo requested to see the doctor, but the receptionist said that Dr. Dobson was not available, and to take the sample to the lab to be analyzed. Deeply troubled about the specimen, Bo responded by saying, "Are you sure? I have never seen anything like this before, and I would like Quin's doctor to see it."

The receptionist went back to speak to Dr. Dobson. She returned and said, "She wants you to drop it off at the lab."

Again, Dr. Dobson did not have the time — not even two minutes — to look at a stool sample that could have explained a lot. To us, the stool sample was highly unnerving, but the doctor's reaction was one of no concern. No curiosity. Why bother to look when you could do a simple lab test. Later, I would find out that the appearance of such a stool could indicate an intestinal blockage.

Natural health expert, Dr. Joseph Mercola, wrote about how the consistency of your stool can give you valuable insight into your health. He describes, "Narrow, pencil-like or ribbon-like stools can indicate a bowel obstruction... and definitely warrant a call to your physician."

We did go to our physician, but again she didn't have time to look at it. Could this have been the moment that changed Quin's outcome? I often wonder why she was so dismissive. She probably didn't start her career that way. As a teacher, I know that students who get into medical school are the brightest and hardest-working. What happens to them after they join an HMO like Kaiser Permanente?

I found a court document that could explain how idealistic and passionate young doctors often are forced to simply comply. Dr. Barbara Zipkin sued Kaiser for negligence of care to patients. She documented that Kaiser doctors are required to see 25 patients in a seven-hour work day (420 minutes) including filling out the necessary paperwork. This averages 16 minutes per patient. If you add the time the doctor spends documenting the visit, this becomes something closer to six minutes per patient. This is hardly enough time to properly diagnose and treat a patient. Even more troubling, physicians routinely face retaliation for failing to adhere to the strict Kaiser patient timelines. This particular doctor was placed on administrative leave for voicing her concerns about the lack of proper patient care.

Other doctors have come forward to state the same thing. The week after Quin died, the wife of a Kaiser doctor recounted a depressing story to my sister. Her husband consistently scored high marks from patients; however, Kaiser's evaluation system scored him low because he spent too much time with patients. A nurse confided in me that at Kaiser award ceremonies, nurses were always surprised to see the doctors who seemed to care the most and spent more time with patients were not recognized.

Four days had passed since we turned in the stool sample. I constantly checked my phone to see if Kaiser had called with the results. I was absolutely sure that this time we would find out what was wrong with Quin. The call finally came in. The stool sample was *only* tested for a bacteria, and it came back negative.

I could not understand. It made no sense to me. Anyone who saw that stool sample would have realized that something was seriously wrong. Could it be that no one actually looked at it?

It was as if they were robots trained to do only one thing. They were not trained to analyze, observe, or be curious. Quin was on an assembly line. A few tests were taken and boxes were checked, that's all.

My son was the victim of patient-churning and I didn't even know it. I had no control over the choices made in my child's name. I suppose it was my misfortune to have picked assembly-line care, but I did not know any better at the time. Now, after years of self-education, I can say that there is a better way.

We need comprehensive ways to address these health concerns. Dr. Thomas O'Bryan states that we need to "Shift from the traditional disease-centered focus (treating the symptoms of the disease) to a more whole patient-centered approach, addressing the whole person, not just an isolated set of symptoms."

He recommends that we investigate the underlying causes of the disease, treating both the symptoms and the causes. Doctors need to be trained to "Listen to their patient's health and family histories, and look for the interplay among genetic, environmental, and lifestyle factors..."

I wish now I had been aware of this information when Quin needed it most.

Chapter Eight
Our Last Christmas Together

It was Christmas Eve, and Quin was spending time with his mother at her house. Conan invited the family over to his mother-in-law's house. His mother-in-law, Carol, such a sweet person, opens her house to us every Christmas Eve. I remember being very sad about Quin and not wanting to socialize. My twin could sense I was uneasy. He came over and asked how Quin was doing.

"Not very well," I told him. "He keeps losing weight and he is in a lot of pain. He is spending a lot of time in the bathroom and doctors can't figure out what's wrong."

Conan was very concerned and wanted to help. We were born two minutes apart. We played sports together and truly felt as if we could read each other's minds. On the soccer field, we were so connected that I knew where he would be and where to pass the ball. We played as one on and off the field. When we bought gifts for family members, everyone would laugh when they saw that we had purchased the same card or present. Most importantly, I felt safe around Conan. He had my back no matter what.

Conan told me about a book that made a big difference in his life. It was a book by the Dalai Lama entitled, *The Art of Happiness*. It influenced his life in a positive way and he wanted to share it with Quin, hoping that it could help him, too.

"Do you think Quin would be receptive to talking to me?" He asked.

"I'm not sure. He has been struggling so much, he doesn't feel much like visiting." I said, "But let's give it a try." We drove over to see Quin.

I called his cell phone and he was in the bathroom, as I expected. I handed Conan the phone.

"Hi, Quin, this is your Uncle Conan. I have a book that I want to share with you, can I give it to you?"

To my surprise, Quin agreed. As we walked into his mother's house, I noticed how long his hair was getting. He wasn't able to get his regular haircut. His pain had disrupted all of his routines. I loved his thick brown hair and how it curled into locks, his favorite beanie keeping them out of his eyes.

My brother and Quin had a great conversation. Conan told him that the book was about seeking spirituality, happiness, and inner compassion.

"Read this book and tell me what you think," Conan said.

Quin agreed and was upbeat about our visit that night. It made me happy, and I hoped that the book might get his mind off his pain for a little while.

There is an ironic twist to this story. The Dalai Lama's, *The Art of Happiness,* was probably not meant for Quin. After Quin passed away, my sister recalls seeing me walk around the house clutching this book. I read it over and over. I annotated it, highlighted passages, and filled it with dozens of colored sticky notes until they protruded from the pages. It was one of the things that got me through the first year. Even today, I refer back to it. I found little pieces of advice that would help get me through the next hour, or the next moment.

I felt hopeful as I left Quin that evening, but I didn't expect that he would want to celebrate the following morning on Christmas Day. Our family tradition is to get together at my parent's house for breakfast and exchange gifts. I called Bo on Christmas morning and wished her a Merry Christmas, and said I would be by shortly to pick up Brianna. To my surprise, she told me Quin was getting ready and wanted to go as well. I was so happy to hear that he wanted to go. Maybe the book that Conan gave him made a difference. Regardless of the reason, knowing that I could be with my children was the best gift I could receive.

Laurie and I drove over and picked them up, and headed over to my parent's house. Quin looked so gaunt and pale, but it didn't matter to me right then. When he walked into the house, he was immediately greeted by my mother, who we call "Nana." She is the matriarch that makes our family strong.

She embraced Quin, and cried because she missed him so much. She took care of Quin when he was a baby, and had always been more than a babysitter to Quin and all of her grandchildren. Growing up, she insisted on daily traditions, like eating her homemade meals around a large table. She didn't care if there were 10 or 25 people, she made sure everyone ate and felt at home. If our conversations escalated to a debate, she insisted that we could disagree and still love each other. When my siblings and I got older, we sometimes talked about moving to a far away city or state, and she always found a convincing way to keep us close. Family is so important to her. Quin could feel her love. He had a smile on his face and seemed to be enjoying himself, despite his pain.

After breakfast, we all gathered around the living room to open presents. It's an ongoing tradition to pick names for a gift exchange. Each gift has to be presented to the recipient with three reasons why they are loved by the gift giver. My sister came up with the idea after one Christmas years ago, when Quin and his cousins were little. That Christmas, they hurriedly opened many presents with joy, but there was an anticlimactic feeling in the air after the last present was opened. The next Christmas, we vowed to initiate this new tradition. This tradition taught our kids the importance of love for family and expressing appreciation.

When it was Quin's turn to open his gift, he was delighted to find something he really wanted, a black pea coat. And then it was time to give him the reasons why he was loved.

I remember Quin's cousin, Connor, telling Quin why he loved him.

"You are like a brother to me. When we were kids you were unbeatable at plastic sword fights. Our imagination took us to fighting Captain Hook in Neverland. We have been playing soccer since we were four, and your skills are impressive. Finally, I love you for being my vacation partner, traveling to Italy, Greece, Ireland, Turkey, Hawaii, England, and backpacking in the Sierra Mountains."

Quin had a huge smile, as he felt the love of his family. This gift, the expression of love, reminded me how fortunate Quin was. He saw so much of the world at a young age. After he passed away, I was comforted by these memories: soccer matches in England, hikes in the Sierra Mountains, snorkeling trips in Maui. When I was at my lowest moments, I had flashbacks of the worst memories that would take me down a path, from which it was hard to return. Then I would look at old pictures and force myself to remember the great memories. I cherish all of these memories, just as I cherish our last Christmas together.

Chapter Nine
Stall Tactics

Twenty-Two Days Before Quin Died

It had been five months since Quin started experiencing health problems. We made another phone call to his primary care physician. We could not wrap our brains around the fact that the stool sample test was negative; we wanted more answers. If the doctor had seen it, she would have known something was seriously wrong. We asked for clarification and if there were any other tests that could be done. She replied curtly, "The stool sample came back negative." She gave no other explanation.

After Quin died, I found the protocol for a proper stool sample analysis. It includes "...microscopic examination, chemical tests, and microbiologic tests. The stool will be checked for color, consistency, amount, shape, odor and the presence of mucus..."

Lab technicians probably did the chemical and microbiological test, but they missed the visual analysis completely. To me, it was obvious that Quin's stool sample was a glaring red flag, but the doctor was simply focused on one thing, a urinary tract infection.

No Referral
Sixteen Days Before Quin Died

Quin's condition was getting worse by the day. Each time we made an appointment to see a doctor, our hope was that this time, finally, they would figure out what was wrong. In addition to the appointments, we tallied over 70 phone calls to Kaiser, in our desperation to find answers.

On one occasion, Dr. Dobson returned our call and left a message. She said she recommended a referral to a gastroenterologist (GI). *Finally!* I thought. Now I had hope that we could get an accurate diagnosis.

There was a cruel twist; however, she made it sound like she had made an actual referral. She didn't. Her exact words were, "recommendation for a GI specialist."

After reviewing Quin's medical records, I did not find that an actual referral was made. She told us that she recommended a referral to a GI specialist, but records show she did not follow through with her own recommendation. It could take months to get an appointment with a specialist. With only 16 days left, even more critical time was wasted with this inefficiency. We were made to believe we had one, but in reality we were just losing valuable time we did not have. We played a back-and-forth game of calling the GI's office and asking for an appointment, only to be referred back to Quin's primary care physician.

Quin's abdominal pain was constant, but at times it intensified drastically. He was struggling more than usual on this day and desperately wanted relief, and asked to see a doctor. We called the appointment line and they scheduled Quin for a same-day appointment. We saw an on-call doctor named Dr. Padova. Of all the doctors to this point, he seemed to have genuine concern for Quin's health problems and spent more time with us than his primary care physician. After reviewing Quin's records and taking into account his symptoms and weight loss, he believed Quin had abdominal inflammation. By this visit, Quin had lost another three pounds. After just one visit, Dr. Padova said it was important that Quin see the GI specialist and made an actual referral.

Dr. Padova was different, he had compassion for Quin. This, in comparison to Quin's primary care physician, who was supposed to provide the high quality, individualized care that Kaiser promotes. Instead, Dr. Dobson offered minimal care and stall tactics. I believe Dr. Padova was new to the system and he had not yet been pressured by the money-saving tactics of the HMO.

Finally, we felt like someone was taking Quin's symptoms seriously. I had such a good feeling about Dr. Padova. I called his office later and asked to talk to him. The staff refused, saying I had to talk to Quin's primary care physician, but I demanded to speak to him. Dr. Dobson had done very little, and in one visit, Dr. Padova took the action while Dr. Dobson stalled.

We finally thought the GI referral was in process, thanks to Dr. Padova. However, his recommendation still needed to be approved by Quin's primary care physician. She didn't follow up. The next day, Bo called the GI's office to make an appointment. But, the receptionist had no information about a referral. Again, Bo was advised to make an appointment with Quin's primary care physician in order to get a referral to see the GI specialist. It felt like more stall tactics.

I sensed no sympathy or willingness to make an effort. It almost seemed like intentional cruelty, knowing how much pain Quin was experiencing. His primary care doctor denied Quin the access to a GI specialist that he so desperately needed.

Right after Quin died, I thought his death had something to do with the lack of care given during those last few days, when he was in excruciating pain. Looking back, I realize it started with his primary care physician, and her complete lack of urgency or curiosity to solve Quin's chronic pain. At the same time, I can't blame her completely. She worked in a system that prevented her from spending any quality time with her patients. How could she possibly make an accurate diagnosis when she is rewarded for the quantity of her care, and not the quality?

Perhaps the medical system she worked in prevented her from ordering more accurate tests or making referrals as a cost-saving measure. What other reason would she have for not actually making the referral? Considering the urgency of the situation, I would have thought that the referral would have been made right away.

After more phone calls, we finally *demanded* the referral to a GI specialist. We were no longer going to accept the stall tactics. We finally got the referral; now we had to wait another month for the actual appointment. We couldn't wait that long. Quin's pain was intensifying. Bo called the GI's office asking for an earlier appointment, but they responded slowly. We waited.

Revealing Clues Ignored
Thirteen Days Before Quin Died

As Quin's symptoms intensified, Bo took him to an urgent care appointment. By chance, Dr. Sabata, a pediatric GI specialist, was there. It seemed like our lucky break; unfortunately, we weren't so fortunate. Despite Quin's tremendous abdominal pain, the doctor didn't seem overly concerned. He told Bo he was not sure what was going on, but they would run some tests. His medical notes state that Quin might have inflammatory bowel disease (IBD). This note was significant. When I looked it up, I found that the symptoms were very similar to Quin's, and that complications may lead a bowel obstruction. The medical examiner later said that Quin died of intussusception, a serious condition in which part of the intestine slides into an adjacent part of the intestine like a telescope, blocking fluid and cutting off the blood supply that can lead to a tear in the bowel, infection, and death of the tissue.

Under psychiatric notes, Dr. Sabata said, "Patient is not nervous or anxious." Quin always did his best to appear calm, even though he was in pain. When a doctor asked him questions, he was honest, direct, and always polite. Looking back, I wish he would not have been so strong. I wish he would have screamed in agony, so they would have taken him seriously.

This was the only time Dr. Sabata saw Quin. Approximately 10 days later, three days before Quin died, Dr. Sabata would enter another note in Quin's medical records stating that Quin needed a psychiatric evaluation.

There were so many mistakes, so many times when Quin's pain, which he evaluated as 11 out of 10, was dismissed. I think this was the moment that sealed Quin's fate. After this, no other doctor would read this note and take Quin's pain seriously.

Apparently, after Quin died, Kaiser staff were talking about what happened. A friend told me that a nurse said, "We are going down for this. We made so many mistakes. The doctors thought that it was all in Quin's head." She pointed to her head, making the mental gesture.

That is why this urgent care visit was so significant. It was the only time the GI specialist saw Quin, and he stated that Quin was not nervous or anxious, days later when another doctor asked for a consult, he replied by saying that it is "psychosocial." In other words, he thought Quin was faking it.

I always thought that living in the United States and having health insurance would protect my family. Kaiser promotes personalized, quality care with good doctors. We saw little evidence of the quality care that they promote.

I found something interesting in Quin's medical records. Dr. Sabata reviewed test results for food allergies, and found Quin had elevated levels of antibodies. Antibodies are part of our defense system that protect us against infection or foreign invaders.

Dr. Tom O'Bryan states, "If you've ever received blood test results with the words 'elevated levels of antibodies,' or 'H' next to the antibody marker, this refers to the fact that the big guns are working overtime to contain a perceived threat, and whether or not you have any symptoms, the tissue damage from the antibodies is accruing."

Quin had an abnormal reading of IgE for wheat grain, which meant there was a 95 percent likelihood of an allergic reaction upon ingestion of this food. He also had elevated IgA antibodies, which meant his immune system was reacting to a threat. High levels of IgA can also point to some chronic infection in the GI tract, inflammatory bowel disease, or celiac disease.

Symptoms caused by eating wheat or gluten include: unexplained weight loss, constipation, diarrhea, cramps, bloating, headaches, acne, fatigue, and depression. Quin had many of these symptoms, and his abnormal antibody results were a red flag that had to be addressed. Not only did multiple doctors from Kaiser ignore the test results, I didn't even know about them until I combed through Quin's medical records after he died. I had no idea that Quin was allergic to wheat, which was probably the trigger of his intestinal inflammation.

Dr. Lopez, our doctor from Mexico, was able to determine that Quin's health issues were related to an intestinal disorder, and possibly related to gluten intolerance or celiac disease. I am amazed Dr. Lopez had the insight to come up with his diagnosis after one visit. But we were never able to go back to see Dr. Lopez, or take his advice, as Quin's condition escalated to an acute level. If doctors from Kaiser would have taken time to connect the dots, or taken his pain more seriously, they could have made an accurate diagnosis, and perhaps changed the course of Quin's fate.

Chapter Ten
"They Didn't Fix Me, Mom."

Quin's Final Week

Quin was with his mother when I received a phone call from her. She was upset.

"He needs to go to the emergency room now, can you take him?"

Quin had unrelenting pain in his abdomen and uncontrollable vomiting. I was only a mile away and rushed over as fast as I could. I ran out of the car and saw he was waiting for me at the door. He could barely stand; Bo was holding him up. I quickly snatched him up in my arms and placed him in the car. He felt so light!

I put the seat back so he could lie down. He was in more pain than he had ever experienced. As I sped off, I knew something was terribly wrong. There was no way we were going to make it to the Kaiser emergency room, so I headed to the nearest hospital, Scripps Mercy Hospital. I was frantic because Quin lost consciousness as I drove. I was screaming at him, "Hold on, Quin! We are almost there!"

I thought he was going to die. I was speeding, going through red lights and honking my horn to alert other drivers. I drove into the Scripps hospital parking lot, stopping right in front of the emergency room entrance. I leaped out of my car, ran to the other side so I could pick Quin up and carry him through the doors. I screamed for help.

"I think my son is dying!"

A door quickly opened and I rushed Quin to the back and onto a hospital bed. Nurses and doctors immediately began working to stabilize him. They gave him a strong pain reliever called Dilaudid, Phenergan for nausea and vomiting, and a sedative. A blood test revealed that Quin had an elevated white blood count. He was given an antibiotic, and the doctor who was attending to Quin explained that the high white blood count could mean that his body was fighting an infection, or that his immune system was compromised. Tests for bacteria in the blood came back negative. The negative blood culture taken at Scripps was significant, because blood cultures taken later at Kaiser came back positive. This could mean that Quin became septic *after* he was transferred back to Kaiser.

Once Scripps' doctors stabilized Quin, they ordered a CAT (CT) scan that showed he had fluid in his pelvis. The doctors noted this was unusual for a patient his age. The physician at Scripps was very attentive, and explained to me that his main concern was the CT scan revealed an intestinal condition called intussusception.

Intussusception is a serious problem that has to be corrected with surgery. The physician believed that Quin had transient intussusception, which means that the problem was intermittent. Transient intussusception could also explain Quin's severe pain and loss of consciousness during the drive to the hospital. I asked the doctor if Quin would need immediate surgery. He said yes, but explained that it would be difficult to get a surgeon there to operate on Quin, because he was a minor. The doctor said they were looking into transporting Quin to Rady Children's Hospital, but that they would have to get Kaiser's approval.

Scripps administration called Kaiser to explain Quin's medical situation and the possibility of transferring him to Rady Children's Hospital. Kaiser *denied* the transfer, instead directing Quin to be transferred by ambulance to Kaiser.

Tragically, this decision probably cost Quin's life. Most hospitals rely on pediatric surgeons in similar situations; Kaiser does not. They wanted to keep Quin's treatment in-house. At Scripps, the doctors considered Quin's situation an emergency. But at Kaiser, there was no sense of urgency; it was business as usual.

This is where knowledge of the law plays a key factor: I *could* have gone straight to Rady Children's Hospital emergency room. They would have been required to treat Quin due to the *Emergency Medical Treatment and Active Labor Act*, also known as the Patient Anti-Dumping statute. Patients cannot be denied emergency care, and a patient may not be transferred if the condition has not been stabilized. I didn't know the law then, but that is why it's vital to learn from my experience.

"I Don't Think They Fixed Me."
Seven Days Before Quin Died

Quin arrived at Kaiser Hospital at 3:00 a.m. The attending surgeon, Dr. Gerund, reviewed Quin's medical chart. He wore red Vans sneakers, and his youthful appearance was a contrast to his confident approach. He explained that Quin needed exploratory surgery. I asked him about the CT scan results from Scripps and that led to the diagnosis of transient intussusception. He said exploratory surgery was necessary to determine the exact nature of

Quin's ailment. With a camera he would make a small incision in the abdomen to look for intestinal problems.

Quin was very hesitant about the exploratory surgery. He had concerns that Kaiser doctors were not sure about what they were doing. I couldn't blame Quin's apprehension. With some convincing from Bo and me, Quin finally agreed. Dr. Gerund said he would be doing the surgery, and that Quin would not be discharged the same day, to ensure the underlying issue that plagued Quin for so long was properly managed. Quin was prepped for surgery and taken into the operating room.

The surgery lasted about an hour. I had been up for 24 hours straight, but didn't feel tired. I was too concerned about Quin to worry about sleep. The surgeon came out to update us on how the surgery went. During the procedure, he found Quin's appendix to be inflamed, and removed it. He also explained that Quin had a *Meckel's Diverticulum*, a flap at the lower end of the small intestine. He went on to say that it was a rare condition that occurs in only two percent of the population, and that it posed no immediate threat to Quin's health and was something that could be treated later. He also stated that he suspected that there were underlying issues that were responsible for Quin's condition and that he wanted gastroenterology to be closely involved with his ongoing treatment. Bo asked the surgeon if the GI was Dr. Sabata, and he responded, "Yes, he is the only pediatric GI specialist at Kaiser."

Quin was placed in recovery for one hour, at which time Dr. Gerund said Quin would be going home and treated on an outpatient basis. Bo reminded him about his initial recommendation of Quin staying longer due to the complications leading up to the surgery. He stated,

"It was such a clean cut appendectomy, we are going to release him early. I saw nothing that appeared abnormal that would give cause for concern."

Bo was surprised, but went to the car to collect some clothes for Quin, filled a prescription for Vicodin and came back to get him. Discharge papers were given, and, less than three hours after surgery, Quin was out the door. While driving home, Bo asked Quin how he was feeling. He turned to his mother and said, "I'm not trying to be pessimistic, but something's still wrong. I don't think they fixed me."

One thing I learned from this experience is the importance of listening to my instincts. Quin's instinct turned out to be correct. They did not fix him. But the doctors had no time to talk to him and ask him how he felt after surgery.

Later that afternoon, Bo called the office of the GI specialist. She spoke to the receptionist and explained that Quin's surgeon wanted Dr. Sabata to follow up with Quin, and she asked for a return call.

Wrong Surgery? Quin is Shamed for Being in Pain
Six Days Before Quin Died

Quin started experiencing pain again, and he described it as the same pain he had before surgery. Bo called and left a message to inform the surgeon that Quin's pain had returned, and that it wasn't post-operative pain.

Quin's pain continued to intensify that same evening to levels that became unbearable, and he began to vomit. I decided to take him back to the emergency room.

He didn't want to go. He knew I had not slept. He knew what the doctor's response would be, but there was no other option. We arrived at 12:30 a.m. and this time we were escorted back very quickly; probably due to Quin having surgery earlier that day.

The attending physician, Dr. Paige, walked in and got on his computer. He didn't look at us. I explained to him that Quin had an appendectomy that morning, but he was in extreme pain and vomiting. He walked over to Quin, and with force pushed down on his abdomen. Quin was still tender from surgery and recoiled in pain.

"Is that necessary?" I asked.

He ignored me. He then very bluntly opinionated that Quin's appendectomy was unnecessary. I was starting to get very angry, but was trying my best to compose myself for Quin's sake. I could not contain the harsh tone in my voice and said, "I want to be clear. Are you telling me that the surgeon did unnecessary surgery on my son?"

He realized I was angry and tried to take his comment back. He went on to say that most teenagers are unable to handle the pain of surgery and complain about it. He said,

"There is nothing I can do. We can keep him overnight and starve him until his surgeon gets here in the morning."

I couldn't believe what I was hearing. I asked him to step outside so I could speak with Quin. When the doctor left, I told Quin I didn't want this guy to put another finger on him, and I would be filing a complaint. However, I wasn't the one suffering from pain. I tried to remain as calm as possible so as not sway his decision. I asked Quin if he wanted to stay. He wanted to go home. I asked him about his pain level and if he could tolerate it. He said that he would do his best.

"Dad, I'm sorry for having you drive me out here again," Quin said.

It made my heart sink. Quin was in obvious distress, but he was worried about me.

"I just want you to get better. Nothing else matters to me right now," I replied.

I called the nurse over and told her we would be leaving, and that I would like to file a complaint on the doctor. She understood and was very accommodating. She said that she needed to get the paperwork for Quin to be discharged, and that it would take a few minutes.

As I was waiting for the nurse, the father of a patient next to Quin on the other side of a curtain came to talk to me. He had a disturbed look on his face. He said that he was at his daughter's bedside and had overheard the way the doctor spoke to Quin. He said he was disgusted by the behavior. He went on to say that he felt especially bad for Quin, as it was obvious that the doctor's heartless words had made Quin feel guilty for making me drive to the hospital.

I later found out that this little girl in the hospital bed next to Quin was suffering from a similar situation. She was a family friend's elementary school student. She had been missing school chronically. When she finally came back to school, the girl's mother told her teacher that her daughter had constant pain and fevers. They dismissed her pain even though the mother went up the ladder of care. Eventually her appendix burst. The mother seemed relieved that she survived, because there was a patient in the same room as her daughter, whose appendix was also removed but ended up dying. My friend recognized the story and knew it was Quin she was talking about.

My head was spinning after our encounter with the latest doctor. Now I had doctors telling me that Quin's surgery was unnecessary and that his pain was not legitimate. On top of that, Quin was feeling guilty about being in pain. I knew deep down something was wrong, but I began to question myself. It reminded me of the term "gaslighting" that came from an old British play. It refers to situations where you question the very instincts that you have counted on your whole life, making you unsure of anything. I became confused. I wanted to believe so much that the doctors were right, and that Quin was okay, regardless of the fact that

Quin was dying.

The nurse brought over Quin's discharge papers and information so that I could lodge a complaint. I could tell she felt bad, and was very nice and helpful. I had a feeling she had dealt with this doctor's rude behavior before. She apologized and we were on our way home. It was 1:30 a.m. and Quin was exhausted. He fell asleep on the way home. When we arrived home, I picked up his fragile body and carried him inside. I prayed, *"Please God, help my son get better."*

The next morning, I called Kaiser Member Services to make a formal complaint. My second phone call was to Dr. Gerund, the surgeon who performed the appendectomy. I informed him that Dr. Paige thought Quin's surgery was unnecessary. Dr. Gerund assured me that the appendectomy was in fact necessary. I asked him, "Why would he say that, then?"

He had no explanation, but to this day I wonder and think back on that moment. As soon as Dr. Paige opened Quin's records on the computer in the exam room he said that Quin's appendectomy was unnecessary. Later, when I looked through the medical records, I found out that Dr. Gerund was not the surgeon at all, as I was led to believe. The person who actually performed the appendectomy was a resident in training, Dr. Koglin. Perhaps it was an opportunity to teach Dr. Koglin how to do an appendectomy. I do not have any proof, but I am still bothered by Dr. Paige's comment. It made me feel like my son was used as a guinea pig.

I asked Dr. Gerund if the appendectomy was the true cause of Quin's failing health. He said that there was something else causing Quin's abdominal pain and the GI would need to address it. He also said that some incisional pain is expected. He advised me to make sure Quin took his pain medication regularly to get ahead of the pain. I felt some relief knowing that he would contact the GI specialist and Quin would be taken care of.

Chapter Eleven
They Think He's Faking It

Four Days Before Quin Died

Quin was in severe pain after surgery, but it wasn't postoperative pain. It was the same agonizing pain he had been having all along. After surgery, I could tell he was trying to man-up. His body was tense and hunched over. He held his stomach, but didn't express his pain as loudly as he should have. Looking back, I think he was hoping the surgery was the answer. But after three days of the same severe pain, he couldn't take it any longer. I recall the expression on his face. He was wincing and so tense. It hurt so much he could not stay in one position for any length of time. The pain medication was not helping.

"What do you think, Quin? Should we go back?" I asked.

Quin replied, "I don't know, Dad. I don't know!"

His face was completely contorted. I could tell he didn't want to go back to the emergency room, where he knew they would tell him the same thing: *"There is nothing wrong with you."*

But he couldn't stand it. "I have to go! I can't handle this pain anymore!"

Once again, we made the trip to the emergency room. As Quin withered in pain, I felt helpless. I was in a constant state of panic, with my instinct telling me my son was dying, yet the doctors dismissed me. I parked the car and walked around to get Quin out. He couldn't walk; I knew I had to carry him in. When he was a toddler I carried him on my shoulders all the time, but when he got a little older, he was too proud and too tough to be carried. Now he was wasting away. I bent over to pick him up. I wanted to scoop him up with strength and urgency, but I knew I had to be gentle. I didn't want to hurt him.

This was not the first time I had to carry my grown son into the emergency room. Rewind-play. Rewind-play. It was the eleventh visit to Kaiser.

Quin was put in a wheelchair. I told the nurse that if Dr. Paige was working, I didn't want him attending to Quin, and that I had filed a complaint against him two nights before. The nurses acknowledged me, and quickly worked to subdue and control Quin's agonizing pain.

Dr. Koglin, the resident who was with the surgeon the day Quin had his appendectomy, examined him. I explained to Dr. Koglin that Quin was in unbearable pain, and that the pain medication was not working. I asked him if he knew what could be causing him so much pain. He had no explanation, but speculated Quin's pain and inability to have a normal bowel movement was due to an *ileus*. An ileus is a blockage of the intestines in the absence of an actual physical obstruction. This type of blockage is caused by the malfunction in the nerves and muscles in the intestine that prevents digestive movement. Dr. Koglin ordered a CT scan of his abdomen. When the medical staff wheeled Quin out, he writhed in agony, twisting and turning to find a comfortable spot in the chair. They gave him more medication to alleviate the pain.

I was up with Quin all night. At 6:30 a.m., Dr. Koglin finally came to Quin's bedside. He said he looked at Quin's CT scan results and said he was backed up all throughout his large intestine and into his small intestine.

He even emphatically stated, "It is impressive!"

His choice of words was odd to me.

Dr. Koglin said they would administer a suppository in order to induce a bowel movement, after which Quin could go home. I was relieved and somewhat reassured by Dr. Koglin's diagnosis. It seemed like a solution was imminent and I could relax a little.

A nurse came in and gave Quin the suppository. When she left, Quin attempted to have a bowel movement, but was only able to excrete a very small amount, with no solid stool. I reported this to the nurse as she prepared the paperwork for Quin to be discharged.

Dr. Koglin came back in, and reassessed Quin's condition and changed his mind. He decided to admit Quin to the hospital for observation. My worry was back.

Once again, I was up all night with Quin. Bo came to relieve me so that I could get some rest, but I was unable to sleep. I was too worried. I called my sister, Ticia, and asked if she could come to the hospital and help Bo and Quin. Without hesitation she came. I knew I could always count on my big sister. She was the one everyone in our family went to when we needed help. Bo and Ticia spent the entire day with him making sure he was comfortable. Someone was with Quin 24 hours a day.

Ticia had no children of her own, so she loved her nieces and nephews as her own. No one in my family ever had to pay for a babysitter. Ticia planned sleepovers with all the kids and even took them on vacations. She spoiled them with her time and also protected them like they were her own cubs. With her and Bo there, I allowed myself to leave Quin's side.

On this day, Quin's medical records indicated that Dr. Gerund asked Dr. Sabata, the GI specialist, to address Quin's ongoing intestinal problems. A few days earlier, Dr. Gerund told us that he felt there was something else going on with Quin's abdominal issues, and that he felt the GI specialist needed to follow up.

Later that afternoon, Dr. Gerund came by to see Quin. Ticia asked him to remain at his bedside to witness first-hand the intense pain he was in after the pain medication wore off. Dr. Gerund responded by saying he believed that there were additional issues that were contributing to Quin's abdominal pain; he guessed it might be a kidney stone. The doctor added that, regardless of the cause, he could do no further testing until Quin had a bowel movement.

"The problem has to resolve itself. All we can do is wait."

He left the room without a physical exam of Quin's abdomen.

Although he had no plan except to wait, it was obvious that he thought it was important enough to contact the GI specialist. Yet, the GI specialist never showed up.

Lack of Urgency Explained
Two Days Before Quin Died

There were several instances where the medical staff failed Quin, but the following entry we found in his medical records after he passed away was the most disturbing. On January 25, 2010, Dr. Gerund wrote:

> I spoke to Dr. Sabata, he feels that no additional work up needed for patient at this time and that there may be a psychosocial element and that the patient may benefit from a psychiatric evaluation as an outpatient.

I thought they were doing everything they could to help Quin. Not until the day I read these words in the medical records, did I realize that the GI specialist refused to see Quin and denied the surgeon's request.

When Dr. Sabata saw Quin earlier, he noted that Quin was psychologically well. But for some reason, he contradicts himself 10 days later, which is hard for me to understand. He didn't physically examine Quin again.

Dr. Gerund seemed to be the doctor in charge of Quin's health plan, but he did not tell us about Dr. Sabata's comments. At the time, I found it odd that every doctor who came in to see Quin in the last few days of his life acted like he was fine. I now understand reading the medical records, that all the doctors who saw Quin believed Dr. Sabata, the expert. They thought Quin was faking it. That explains the lack of urgency while Quin writhed in pain. It explains the lack of action, even though Quin's body was shutting down.

When Quin died, I was so numb. I didn't know why he died, and I didn't blame anyone. I just wanted to find out the truth. In going through Quin's medical records, we enlisted a family friend, Sherri, who is a registered nurse. At one point she stopped and exclaimed,

"Oh my God! I can't believe this!"

"What?" I asked.

"They thought it was in his head! They fucking thought he was faking it!" she replied.

I realized in that moment that maybe my son didn't have to die. I realized in that moment that my gut instinct was right all along. My son was dying. I knew it, but at the time the doctor's response was making me feel like I was the crazy one.

Even Opiates Can't Control His Pain

Quin had been instructed not to eat or drink until he had a bowel movement. He had neither eaten one bite of food, nor taken one sip of water in two days. He was so hungry and thirsty. I was at his bedside all night trying to comfort him. His pain was severe and the pain medication had no effect at all. The medication was designed to relieve pain for two hours, but the moderating effect of the medication meant that the relief lasted less and less each time.

In the week since his appendectomy, he had received a series of pain medications, each one stronger than the last, to help relieve his increasing pain. He progressed from Vicodin to Norco to Morphine to Dilaudid. These strong medications that could completely cease the pain of a woman in labor, did not make a dent in Quin's level of pain.

In a first-person account of the power of the opiate drug Dilaudid, former police Chief Kyle J. Fittro, recounted, "Let me tell you a story about the power of Dilaudid, or as some people call it, hospital heroin." Upon receiving a shot for a serious medical condition he said, "I could immediately feel the drug move up my arm, through my brain... An intense euphoric sensation that took away all the pain and made everything alright..."

He later heard other people describe the high of an opiate like Dilaudid as, "The house could burn down with me in it, and that would be just fine."

I now wonder how my son endured such pain, when an opiate as strong as Dilaudid had absolutely no effect.

I Begged the Doctor to Save My Son
One Day Before Quin Died

By 6:00 a.m. the next morning, the effect of the pain medication would only last about 10 minutes. Quin was going on his third day without food or water. He had an IV in his arm to keep him hydrated, but it was extremely difficult. I constantly had a cup of ice for him, and spread the ice on his lips, but made sure he did not swallow any of it. He was constantly nauseated and dry heaving. I couldn't believe nurses and doctors thought that Quin's condition was normal. *"Was I the crazy one? Is this business as usual?"*

It was 8:30 a.m. when Dr. Koglin came into the room to examine Quin. I updated him on the severity of Quin's pain, and how difficult the night had been for Quin not being able to sleep. Dr. Koglin appeared puzzled, and had no explanation for Quin's condition.

I was very clear in explaining the severity of Quin's pain to Dr. Koglin. Incredulously, he writes in Quin's medical records,

"Quin is doing well with decreased pain."

Right about that time, Dr. Gerund walked in and examined Quin as well. He said that Quin would be getting an X-ray. I was so concerned and scared, I pulled Dr. Gerund out into the hallway, so I could talk to him privately. My instincts were screaming at me. I tried holding back my emotion, but tears fell from my eyes as I pleaded,

"Dr. Gerund, I'm very worried about Quin. I'm afraid we are losing Quin and his body is giving up on him. Promise me that you are going to do everything possible for him,"

Dr. Gerund replied, "I will. I promise."

I took a deep breath. He responded with sincerity. He was on my side. He would take care of Quin. I wiped the tears from my eyes and composed myself before I walked back into the room. Right about that time, Bo and Ticia showed up to relieve me, and take over for the day. I told Quin I loved him and gave him a kiss on the forehead. I told him I would be back later that evening.

Upon review of Quin's medical records, both Dr. Koglin and Dr. Gerund reviewed Quin's lab results after this visit with him. Quin's white blood count took a dramatic shift to the left. Although I didn't know it at the time, this was a turning point.

Sherri helped us read through Quin's medical records. She explained what it means when a patient's white blood count dramatically shifts to the left.

"I can't believe they didn't catch this! Quin's white blood count shifted to the left to 2.1!," she said.

"What does that mean?" I asked.

"A left shift in most cases means there is a severe bacterial infection. I can't believe they didn't put him on antibiotics right away!"

Dr. Koglin didn't see this as a serious red flag. Instead he wrote into the medical records, "White blood count is at 2.1, lab error? Will re-check tomorrow."

Dr. Koglin thought it was a lab error. Dr. Gerund read the same report as well, and although he suspected an infection, he did not order antibiotics. In the medical notes he wrote, "wbc 2.1 suggests some infectious process is going on and without a clear cause I am hesitant to start patient on antibiotics. Ordering blood cultures."

Both doctors reviewed the same blood test, both come up with different conclusions, and neither ordered lifesaving antibiotics. Yet another mistake. The research I did later confirmed Sherri's opinion. A left shift could mean a bacterial infection, sepsis, or tissue necrosis. All this was confirmed later by the autopsy report. Quin's medical records indicated his blood cultures came back positive for a staph infection. A staph infection can turn deadly if it enters the bloodstream. Treatment generally involves fighting the infection with antibiotics.

A Vision: "Take me instead!"

It was 9:00 a.m. when I got home. I should have been tired considering I had only had five hours of sleep in three days, but I could not sleep. I had a cup of coffee and sat down in the living room. What happened next was probably the most spiritual moment I've ever had in my life.

At this point, nobody thought Quin was going to die, not even the doctors. As I was sitting on the couch, I felt the presence of my grandfather, Pop, who passed away when Quin was 5 years old. He was one of the most important people in my life. He read us bedtime stories, played catch with us, and taught us how to swim. I always felt so safe when he was around. His family was his number one priority in life.

I suddenly felt Pop in the room with me. I had never felt anything like it before. He spoke to me.

"Brian, I am here to take Quin."

I remember the fear and sadness that entered my body. I responded, "No, you cannot take him."

"I am here to take Quin," he said again.

Tears started to flow from my eyes and I said, "You can't take him, take me instead!"

Pop told me that he couldn't take me because it wasn't my time. I pleaded with him one last time, "Please, take me!"

Just as sudden as his presence appeared to me, he was gone. I wasn't sure what had just happened, but it was like a waking dream that lasted about 20 seconds. Doubt set in and I considered the possibility of losing Quin. I rejected the thought.

Quin is not going to die! Yes, he is sick, but doctors reassured me he would be fine and they were going to take care of him, I thought.

When Laurie came home, I wasn't sure I wanted to mention it, but when she saw the look on my face, she knew I was upset.

"Something just happened to me, but I don't think I can tell you. I don't know if I should tell you," I said.

I couldn't bring myself to say it out loud. I was afraid to talk about it, because I didn't want it to happen. Laurie asked, "You can tell me, what is it?"

I was leery, but I finally told her that Pop came to me, and relayed his message. She comforted me and said, "Quin is not going to die. He is going to be okay."

Chapter Twelve
Quin Shares His Happiest Memory

The Kaiser Complaint Department called me to follow up on my complaint regarding Quin's treatment in the emergency room by Dr. Paige. Laurie was next to me and could hear the man on the phone and his calm response as I pleaded for help. She couldn't restrain herself and asked for the phone. At that moment, she spoke for everyone with determination, as if to say, *this ends now.*

"Quin is deteriorating! We are asking for help and no one is listening! We want him moved to another hospital. What is the process to get him moved to another hospital?"

The person on the line responded calmly, "I will make note of your concerns, but I can assure you that doctors and nurses are doing everything possible to help him."

He had no way of knowing what the doctors were doing or not doing. He was trained to respond in a dispassionate manner, and he did his job well.

We were finally determined. We decided that day that if his condition did not improve by the next day, we were going to leave Kaiser and take him to another hospital. We could no longer accept the advice that, "All we can do is wait."

January 26, 10:50 a.m.: Bo and Ticia continued to press the nursing staff, pointing out Quin's deteriorating condition. They specifically pointed out that he had lost so much weight, his eyes were sunken in. He was so weak, he couldn't walk without help. He was in so much pain, he could not sleep. The nurses assured them that someone would come by to address their concerns.

The registered dietitian for Kaiser entered Quin's room to assess him. Ticia asked him if Quin could receive some type of nutritional supplements to keep him going. The dietitian told Ticia that she would have to address the issue of supplementing Quin with IV nutrition with the doctor who was scheduled to stop by later. Quin's medical records by the dietitian state, "Patient meets malnutrition criteria, will alert MD through dear doctor note."

The nutritionist agreed that Quin met the malnutrition requirement, but he also had no sense of urgency.

After this, Bo called the pediatric nurse manager to express her displeasure with Quin's care. She left a message for her explaining that something needed to be done immediately to help Quin and that the GI doctor had failed to come and evaluate him.

At approximately 2:00 p.m., another doctor came into Quin's room, Dr. Kearney. Bo and Ticia told him that Quin had not eaten since his surgery (six days), and that he had lost even more weight. Dr. Kearney did not perform any kind of physical exam, and instead responded by saying, "All we can do is wait. He does not need any IV nutrition, people can live quite some time without food."

The doctor appeared annoyed by Bo's and Ticia's persistence. He refused to comment further and left the room.

Dr. Gerund, Quin's surgeon, kept on telling us that the GI specialist, Dr. Sabata, needed to evaluate Quin's condition. At this point, we had no idea that Dr. Sabata actually had no plans to evaluate Quin; making the excuse that he needed to see a psychiatrist instead.

Bo was tired of waiting and decided to call Dr. Sabata directly to find out why he had not come in as requested. She was told by an assistant that he was unavailable, but that she would leave him a message to contact her upon his return.

5:30 p.m.: The revolving door kept on opening and closing with different doctors, but no results. The next person to come in was a physician's assistant. He repeated the same refrain all the other doctors were repeating. In his opinion, "Quin's physical ailments derived from and ileus and that all would resolve itself in a day or two."

Ticia then told him, "This has been an ongoing issue. It has been chronic for weeks before the surgery and nobody has been listening to us. I want you to tell me that you are listening to me, and I want you to repeat what I said!"

He seemed put off and responded, "You've made it perfectly clear."

6:30 p.m.: Quin's Cousin Connor and Aunt Maria Visit Quin

Quin's cousin and aunt walked in the room, and saw him for the first time since New Year's Eve. Maria recalled her first impression upon walking in was, *Is he dying?*

He was skeletal and looked similar to pictures she had seen of concentration camp survivors. She immediately ran to him, kissed him, and held his hand. Quin's cousin, Connor, sat next to him and started talking to him about funny videos. Bo observed quietly and said, "I'm glad you are here. That's the first time I've seen him smile in a long time."

Hours Before Quin Died

8:30 p.m.: I arrived to the hospital to find Bo, Ticia, Maria, and Connor with Quin. Quin was in the recliner chair and Maria was next to him. She wanted to get his mind off of the pain and she asked him, "Quin, what is your happiest memory?"

Quin said it had to be his trip to England to see his favorite soccer team, Manchester United, play in a soccer match. Quin reflected and recalled the moment. He was on the train from London to Portsmouth. He looked out the window and saw the countryside, green rolling hills, pastures, and trees. The anticipation of seeing his favorite soccer players, Cristiano Ronaldo and Wayne Rooney, was palpable.

Connor and Quin at the Manchester United match in Portsmouth, England

I remember that trip so well. It was two years earlier. Quin was 14 years old and healthy. Laurie and I had decided to take Quin and Connor to Ireland and England. Quin was so excited, because it had always been his dream to go to a Manchester United game. As we walked into the stadium, the Manchester players were warming up right in front of us. Quin and Connor walked down as close as they could to the players and took some pictures. We did not sit down the entire game. We were shouting and chanting along with the other Manchester fans. We had so much fun that day. After the game, Quin couldn't stop talking about it, saying it was the single greatest day of his life.

Quin Collapses: "It's of No Concern."

Talking about his happiest moment seemed to distract Quin from the pain for a moment. Soon his face winced and tightened again. He wanted to move back to his bed. Connor and I picked him up, holding him up by his arms. He walked slowly and every move seemed to cause pain. Suddenly, his body went limp and he lost consciousness. He collapsed in our arms. Connor and I carried him back to his bed and we quickly summoned help.

Maria again recalled, *Is this it? Is he dying?* But we could not allow that thought to enter our minds.

Two nurses entered the room and administered oxygen. The nurses hooked him up to monitors that showed his resting heart rate to be 140. Quin was an athlete. In September, when he first started feeling ill, his resting heart rate was 55.

Quin finally regained consciousness. Maria noticed Quin's feet were distorted, curled up, and cramped. She pointed it out to the nurse who quickly straightened them out.

Yet another doctor, Dr. Massi, was on duty when this occurred. He entered the room with a calm and normal pace. He didn't look over at Quin, but he asked the adults in the room a few questions. He concluded that Quin passing out was due to him walking about, and to be expected and of no concern. He also attributed it to dehydration. The doctor addressed our concerns by saying, "He seems fine now."

Looking back, it is hard to imagine that Quin was hours from death. He was literally in the death process and no one saw it. I felt it. My sisters and Bo felt it. The doctors contradicted our greatest fears. They told us, "Quin is fine. He is healthy. We just have to wait for a bowel movement. We have to wait for the problem to resolve itself."

Quin's medical records indicated that the head nurse asked Dr. Massi if Quin should be transferred to higher level of care. This means that she believed that Quin needed to be moved to the Intensive Care Unit (ICU), where he could receive critical care. Dr. Massi refused. Instead, he writes in Quin's medical record: "Quin is healthy. Patient had a fainting spell, anxiety."

He ordered Quin to be given Klonopin, as needed for sleep. Quin died within hours of his assessment of being healthy and fainting due to "anxiety." Again, we now wonder if Dr. Sabata's note influenced Dr. Massi: "...patient may benefit from a psychiatric evaluation as an outpatient."

Chapter Thirteen
The Final Journal Entry: Part II

Back to the Beginning
Journal Entry: January 26, 2010

10:00 p.m.: Maria asks if we can say a prayer together before she leaves. Quin nods his head. Maria opens a book of prayers. We place our hands on Quin and pray.

"Please heal me Lord...Please give me a miracle. Please give me hope. Please give me peace. Lift me up beyond the regions of my pain and despair. Prepare each cell to be born anew into health and happiness, peace and love...I accept your will for me, I accept your healing, I accept your love..."

11:00 p.m.: I am getting ready to start my shift alone. Before Ticia leaves she asks, "Will you be okay? Do you want me to stay, Brian?"

Ticia was with Quin all day, over 12 hours.

"I'll be okay, Ticia. Go and get some sleep. But tomorrow, if Quin doesn't get better, we're getting him out of here."

My sister agrees. Everyone leaves and I am alone, standing by Quin's bed doing everything I can to make him comfortable. He cannot sleep and his pain gets worse by the minute. I spend every moment adjusting his pillow, moving him, talking to him; anything I can to help him deal with his pain. I feel so helpless, but I keep trying. Quin needs to have a bowel movement. That is the only medical advice Kaiser staff could give us. I help Quin to the bathroom and he tries his best, but cannot make himself go.

The words, "All we can do is wait until he has a bowel movement" are like a broken record.

January 27, 1:00 a.m.: I help Quin sit on the toilet. He stoops over and I can see his bones protruding through his skin. He uses every ounce of strength to have a bowel movement. Even now, he shows his competitiveness, trying his best to will himself to have a bowel movement, the one thing the doctors tell Quin he has to do to get well. Quin looks up at me. His face is almost white. He says, "Dad, can you wipe and check to see if there is anything? I can't do it."

Quin is so crippled by his pain he is unable to wipe himself and that crushes me, yet I can see in his eyes how brave he is. He still wants to fight. I see the same persistence he has on the soccer field.

I want to believe what the doctors have said over and over, "He's going to be fine."

3:30 a.m.: Quin's pain is so severe, he is desperate to find a position to alleviate his pain.

"Dad, can you take me to the visitation room?"

It's only a few steps across the hall. There is a recliner in there. Maybe that will help. Nothing helps. A nurse comes in and asks us to go back to bed.

"Is the doctor coming?" I asked.

The nurse replies, "He said he'll be up soon. Let's get you back to bed."

4:00 a.m.: I notice the nurses look more panicked. Dr. Wren is still not responding to the nurses requests. They ask for the nurse in charge. They are moving more quickly. Their gestures to each other seem more sharp. I hear mumbling outside the door, and they steal glances at each other; or is it my imagination?

The Moment I Lost Quin

A half an hour later, 4:30 a.m., is the moment I realized I lost Quin. I replay the details constantly.

The part I recall most vividly, is the moment I was holding Quin and I knew for sure he was dying.

After many attempts to get Dr. Wren to come to Quin's bedside, he finally came in. He seemed annoyed. *I took him away from something more urgent, perhaps?* In the medical records, it indicated the nurses requested for him to come, but he ignored their requests. His response was, "Be up later."

The nurses requested him so many times, they finally said, "Is there another doctor available?"

When he finally strolled in, I was already in full panic mode. I gestured urgently with my hands for him to come over. Dr. Wren moved slowly. At that moment, Quin started projectile vomiting. I cradled him and placed him back on his bed. I looked up at Dr. Wren to help me: "Do something!"

He stood there, doing absolutely nothing. His face and body appeared frozen. Nurses frantically ran around him to get what they needed.

As I looked back down at Quin, I cradled him in my arms and fixed my gaze on him. He took a deep breath, one more gasp of air. His eyes rolled back into his head.

"Hold on Quin! Hold on! I love you!"

I knew that was the moment I lost him. It was 4:30 in the morning on January 27.

After they called a code blue, I could not keep track of all the doctors and nurses who stormed in and out. This was the *first* time I saw a concerted effort and a sense of urgency from anyone at Kaiser; it was too late. I stood on a chair to keep my eyes on Quin. Doctors and nurses surrounded him and tried to resuscitate him, inserting a tube and doing heart compressions. For a while they ignored me completely. It was as if I was invisible—a ghost in the room. I wanted to be there, but I knew I probably shouldn't be there. Then, suddenly, I was visible to them again.

A nurse, who I had never seen before said, "We should get the father out of here." Someone else in the room responded sharply, "Just let him be with his son!"

Someone in that room was *defending* Quin and me. Someone had compassion for us, and it was a new feeling. In contrast, I still get sick to my stomach when I think of Dr. Wren. I later read his version of events in the medical records:

> Upon arrival, patient trying to get out of bed with father assisting, then patient with massive emesis (vomiting), immediately turned patient to right side.

Correction, Doctor: Quin was not trying to get out of bed. Dr. Wren did not assist him onto his right side after vomiting. *I* was the one assisting Quin, while *he* stood there uselessly.

The moment I lost Quin is permanently seared into my memory. The doctors say I have post-traumatic stress from the images of this moment, but for me it's just the last day I had with my son. No one sees my pain. I'm really good at hiding it. I don't want to bother anyone. I tell myself that if Quin went through so much pain, I can get through this pain, too.

My only son, Andrew Quinlan Murphy, took his last breath at Kaiser Permanente Hospital on the fourth floor, as I cradled him. It wasn't until later that I realized the irony of that moment. It seemed like a short time ago, 16 years to be exact, Quin was born at Kaiser Permanente Hospital, on the fourth floor, and moments after he was born, I cradled him.

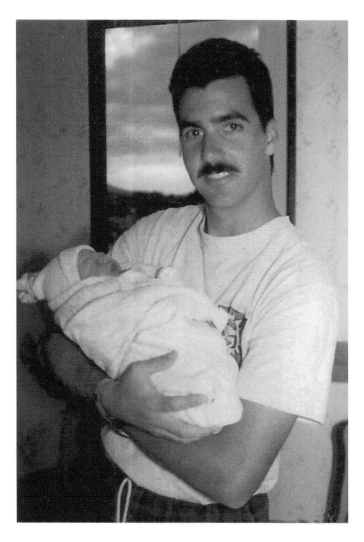

Chapter Fourteen
Saying Goodbye

Before I left the hospital, I walked over to Quin's body to say goodbye. His eyes were closed, and he looked like he was sleeping peacefully, finally, without pain. I put my hand on his chest, and gently gave him a kiss on his forehead and told him I loved him. I turned and walked out of the room. Tears streamed from my eyes on the long walk away from Quin, holding only his beanie.

Laurie was holding me as we walked out of the hospital. I was in a daze and my legs were weak. I thought I was going to faint and can remember Laurie crying, telling me to hold on.

"We are almost to the car," she said.

Instead of helping Quin into the car, Laurie was helping me.

My Family Holds Vigil Over Quin's Body

Bo and the rest of my family remained at the hospital, standing in the hallway, not knowing what to do next. Bo's sobs echoed throughout. A hospital employee walked up to Bo and asked, "Are you the mother?"

She opened a door and guided the family into a quiet waiting room. She helped Bo sit in a chair and knelt before her, gently holding her hands and looking into her eyes. "Can we pray together?"

Bo closed her eyes and nodded her head. Her sobs lessened as the woman prayed, "Thank you, Father Jesus. Thank you for taking our brother home…"

She was like an angel. Her prayers soothed Bo as everyone circled around them and held hands. Bo stayed there while my mother, father, sisters Ticia and Maria, and older brother Sean went back to watch over Quin until the medical examiner took possession of his body.

Dr. Gerund, the surgeon who remained on Quin's case, walked in. He expressed his condolences. Ticia turned to him and said, "I guess waiting for the issue to resolve itself didn't work so well."

Dr. Gerund was still unable to articulate an explanation for Quin's death, aside from the astonishingly obvious declaration that, "There must have been something really bad in his stomach."

It seemed odd to those in the room that he said this in layman's terms, like a parent's simplistic explanation to a small child.

The head nurse walked in. She said the nursing team requested to pray with my family. My family agreed. The nurses walked in looking distraught. My sister touched Quin's brown locks of hair as they prayed; the Lord's Prayer and the Hail Mary prayer. She looked up to see tears streaming down the nurses faces. My sister recalled a moment of solidarity with these nurses. They seemed crushed too.

As my family stayed with Quin's body, Laurie drove us home. I can't describe what shock feels like, only that I felt numb and completely lost. I knew nothing would ever be the same. Quin was dead, and I felt dead too. My body was here, but I was completely lost in a painful nightmare. My head was bowed, my gaze blurry and downcast. As Laurie turned the corner to our street, I looked up.

I saw black crows all around our property. There must have been 40 of them; they were on top of our house, on our lawn, and on the sidewalk. They were neither flying around nor squawking; they were silent and still. I had never seen so many crows by our property before, and I found it odd that of all days, they were there the day Quin had passed away. For two days, the crows hung around the house, and then they just disappeared.

I read that crows have a symbolic meaning. They guide souls from the realm of the living to the afterlife. Some consider the crow has powerful knowledge of the changes in life and death. When the crow appears, it can be a spiritual blessing and a special message from the one who has passed away, or a profound confirmation that your loved one has just been reborn.

I found myself constantly looking for signs. I was desperately looking for something that would connect me to Quin. The grief was so overwhelming, all I wanted to do was hold him. I wanted to believe in some way that Quin was trying to communicate with me, and let me know he was okay.

Laurie helped me up the steps to our house. I fell onto the sofa and covered my head. I wanted to disappear alone in my grief. Laurie felt my pain and held me tight, not wanting to let me go.

The Power of a Tribe

Before I had left the hospital, my sister asked, "Should we come over?"

"No," I replied. "I just want to be alone."

Little did I know that after I left, my family discussed it and decided as a group that they could not let me be alone. Within one hour, people started to arrive at my house; my four siblings, nephews, nieces, aunts, uncles, former coaches, and my best friends since grade school. I sat on the couch and I was surrounded. Everyone had a hand on me, touching me, as if their magical touch would stop me from dying myself. They wouldn't leave my side.

I thought I wanted to be alone, but I realized that I needed them. I had not slept for three days, so there would be moments when I would close my eyes and sleep. Then my eyes would open and I would remember.

My sister said that I was surrounded in these moments. My aunt was kneeling in front of me in those rare moments when I fell asleep, staring at my face. When I opened my eyes she noticed that horrific expression on my face after waking. My face went from calm and quiet to distorted with pain and quiet sobs. My aunt held my face with her hands. Everyone came to me and touched me, held me.

This scene describes my continued struggle. My first inclination is to be alone and to isolate myself. I don't want to let people see my grief. Alone, I can be myself. I can have outbursts in my solitude without worrying that I'll be judged for having a mental breakdown. Alone, I can look for signs without distractions. But family and friends kept me afloat. They were my *moai*, my lifelong circle of friends and family. Okinawans, who live long, happy lives, maintain these strong social networks to support each other. This provides, "...emotional support in times of need and [can] give all of their members the stress-shedding security of knowing that there is always someone there for them."

I could not have made it without my *moai*. My older brother Sean, didn't ask, "What can I do to help?" He just showed up at my door. "Let's go. I'm taking you somewhere," he said. I didn't even have time to consider that I might not want to go. He took me to the park by the bay where our grandfather, Pop, used to take walks everyday. Not until I got there and retraced Pop's steps did I feel grateful to my brother for forcing me out of my dark bedroom. Sean loves being out in nature, and somehow knew that it would be healing.

So even today, when my friends and family reach out to me, I have to make a choice. Do I remain in my solitary world, where I can be closer to Quin, or do I rejoin the tribe?

Broken Heart

It was as if my role with Quin had switched. While he was struggling, I was his attendant, his advocate, his strength. Now, however, I was the one who was broken. Before Quin died, he constantly wore a San Diego Chargers football beanie, that his cousin, Jeff, had given him for Christmas. He wore it every day, and it still smelled like him. When I slept, I put it under my pillow. During the day, I kept it in my back pocket. Each time I looked at it, I was reminded of how I adjusted it on his head while he was in the hospital. I held on to it as if it were the last part of him that still existed.

I wanted to be with Quin. Before I experienced this, just the simple thought of losing a child was enough to knock the wind out of me. But with the reality of it, I felt like I was suffocating and my body was squeezing in. My heart felt like it was being crushed under tremendous pressure. It wasn't just my mind that was in turmoil; my physical body felt constantly besieged. Even my sleep was disturbed. Every morning I was startled awake at exactly 4:30 a.m., the moment that Quin died in my arms; the moment I placed him back into bed and he took one final breath. This is how every morning began for me. The pain was so strong, I would have done anything to make it go away. But the only thing that would make it go away, would be to no longer exist myself. I had no purpose, and the desire to end my misery outweighed my desire to live.

One day, I came perilously close to ending my pain. I was thinking of Quin. When he was a toddler, he was obsessed with pirates. After watching the sword fighting scene in *Peter Pan* he began to dress like a pirate, talk like a pirate, and carry his plastic swords everywhere he went. As he got older, he began reading adventure fiction novels like, *The Lord of the Rings* and *Eragon*. We replaced his plastic swords with a fine collection of replicas like, Anduril, the sword of King Elessar of Gondor. We kept them safely behind a glass case, and it was all connected to his imagination and his love of reading.

I was missing my little pirate and the boy who turned into an avid reader. I stared at one of his swords and I picked it up. I thought, *I will never see Quin again. I will never hug him again.* This very real thought was too much for my heart to take. I removed the protective sheath and put the sharp point to my chest. At first, it just touched the skin, but I started to put pressure on it. I was crying. I wanted to die. I pressed down harder and harder, and I started to cut through the skin. I felt a sense of relief, like I was stabbing the loss. I was literally killing the grief. By killing myself, I would kill the unbearable daily anguish.

I don't know what stopped me. I thought about disgracing Quin's memory. I knew I would compound the tragedy and hurt my family. I would create more suffering, if I followed through with my desire to end the pain. I put the sword back in its sheath and took a deep breath. *What just happened?* It was an impulsive act.

Research on suicide confirms that attempts are typically not long-planned deeds, often happening in a moment of heightened vulnerability. Having lethal weapons easily accessible does not diminish the impulse itself, but does improve the deadly outcome. I narrowly avoided another tragedy, but my heart was still broken.

Not long after that day, I was startled awake from another nightmare at exactly 4:30 in the morning. This morning, however, was different. It felt like a stabbing sharp knife was going through my chest. I generally have a high threshold for pain, but this pain was something that I had never experienced before. The left side of my body, my arm and leg, felt numb. I was clutching my chest as I tried to get out of bed. As I put my feet on the ground, I collapsed to the floor. Laurie woke up to find me on the ground and screamed.

"Brian, what's wrong!?

My chest felt like it was being squeezed under tremendous pressure, and I was gasping for air.

Laurie rushed me to the emergency room, where I was immediately assessed. A nurse interviewed me. I explained my symptoms, as well as the recent loss of my son. The nurse looked at me with compassion in her eyes.

"You need to look up broken heart syndrome. It's a real thing," she said.

The test results showed my heart was fine. Maria came to my bedside while I was hooked up to machines.

"Brian, before I came here I had a strong premonition. It's not your time yet. There is still something more you have to do."

After I was released, I looked up the Mayo Clinic's definition of broken heart syndrome:

> ...a temporary heart condition that's often brought on by stressful situations, such as the death of a loved one... People with broken heart syndrome may have sudden chest pain... and may be caused by the heart's reaction to a surge of stress hormones...

This confirmed that I was not dying that morning. When I thought it was the end for me, I felt that same, strange sense of relief. Finally, the pain I felt would be gone.

I was turning all of my pain inward, as if I was the only one suffering. It was becoming about me, and not about Quin, and I could not allow that to happen. I knew there was something I needed to change. My purpose was not yet clear, but I knew it couldn't be about my suffering alone.

Then I remembered a quote from the Dalai Lama, "It is under the greatest adversity that there exists the greatest potential for doing good, both for oneself and others."

I didn't really know what that meant. I found it hard to see past my endless grief. I could not imagine that something good could come from losing my son. While I wasn't ready to move on, a small seed had been planted.

Chapter Fifteen
Turning to Family

I felt perilously close to losing myself. I was at a critical moment, and I didn't know where I was going. I could have easily given up, but there was one thing that helped me hang on. It was the vision I had of my grandfather, Pop, the day before Quin died. Pop told me he was there to take Quin. At the time, Pop's message was terrifying, and I rejected it. But now, his message brought me comfort. I felt that he had come to me, to let me know Quin would be safe with him. This was the one thing that I could cling to.

Quin's Namesake

My family and a few friends went to visit Pop's grave at Fort Rosecrans National Cemetery in San Diego. Pop was buried next to his father, John E. Murphy, an Irish immigrant who won the Congressional Medal of Honor. His birth name was Andrew Quinlan. He was 9 years old when he was sold to the British Navy as an indentured servant. He worked as a cabin boy, and one of his jobs was to serve the officers tea. If he spilled even one drop, he would receive a brutal lashing. The experience toughened him.

As he grew older, he learned how to sail. While he had contempt for the sailors who mistreated him, they didn't break his spirit. He was patient and waited for the right time to rebel.

After years of servitude, he found his chance. One night, as the ship was docked in New York, he knocked out the night guardsman and escaped. He was 18 years old and now free in America. To protect himself from being caught, he changed his name from Andrew Quinlan to John Edward Murphy, taking his mother's maiden name. This story was epic in our family. It was an anchor story that defined us.

Quin was named after my great-grandfather. On the morning of June 3, 1993, when Quin was born on the fourth floor of the hospital, we already had another name picked out, a girl's name. The doctors told us we would be having a girl, so that is what we had planned. I was shocked, yet happy when we saw Quin. The first thing we had to figure out was a new name. I met my family for breakfast and we brainstormed ideas. Great-grandfather's name was suggested. I knew it was the right name when my grandfather, Pop, beamed with approval. We even decided what his nickname would be Quin.

Quin was tough like his namesake. They both had the same fighting spirit, a sense of fairness, and the same tenacious attitude to never give up, no matter how tough things were. My great-grandfather was a POW who spent much of his time boxing to entertain the guards and other prisoners. Later, I found out that the mission he was on, that won him the Congressional Medal of Honor, took place on June 3, 1898, almost 95 years before Quin was born.

These little coincidences gave me comfort. My great-grandfather's strength and Quin's fighting spirit are part of me. I think back on Quin's last days and how he held it together, despite describing his pain as an 11 out of 10. When I'm in unbearable emotional pain, I think of how Quin handled his own pain. If he handled it with such grace, then maybe I can too.

The Wake: "I Was Lifted Up."

I have heard the saying, "I was lifted up," but I never knew how it felt until the day of Quin's wake. Two days after Quin died, we had a wake at my sister and brother-in-law's house. By word of mouth, about 400 people showed up. My wife, Laurie, put her arm around me as we walked towards the house. I felt too weak, too overwhelmed. I hesitated at the door.

"I don't think I can do this," I said.

With tears in her eyes, Laurie said, "Everyone is here, we can do this together."

I hadn't seen my daughter, Brianna, since Quin died. For two days she was at her grandmother's house. I was worried about her and anxious to see her. The moment she walked in, we spotted each other. She ran towards me and jumped into my arms. She started crying as I held her tight. Her aunt whispered in my ear, "That's the first time she has cried."

My family was waiting for me at the door. They saw my hesitation to come in, so they gently held me and escorted me in. When I walked into the backyard, I couldn't believe what I saw. Hundreds of people were there for Quin, for me, for all of us. Quin's teachers were there; his very first preschool teacher; his last teacher; his soccer coaches; and his friends. My childhood friends and my coaches throughout my life were also there. The community that we had built was there. The priest who baptized Quin was the same priest who memorialized his short life. Afterwards, the tears turned into a joyous celebration and a glorious send-off that lasted into the dark hours of the next morning.

During Quin's wake, I had two opposing feelings that seemed

impossible to coexist. Miraculously, at the very same moment that I was feeling the worst depths of grief I had ever felt in my life, I also felt love and joy. In one moment, the thought that I would never see Quin again would enter my mind. That reality was a crushing blow. Then, in the next moment, I simply had to look up. I cannot describe to you what it looks like when people transfer their energy to you. You can't see it. You can only feel it. And in that moment, I felt blessed. I felt like I was floating, and I thought, *They are lifting me up.*

My sister and I often talk about this day. She remembers glancing over at me to see how I was doing. I was standing in the kitchen surrounded by my childhood friends. We had known each other since elementary school, little league, and all of the teams where we had bonded as brothers. I was standing in the middle of the group, and although I didn't know it at the time, they were in tune with me, watching my every expression and gesture. They comforted me with our shared stories, giving me a sense of normality. Their sarcastic banter and well-timed zingers made me laugh. I even felt guilty about it. How can I smile at a time like this? I thought. Looking back, though, I know they were doing everything in their power to give me respite; a short period of relief. My grief would return the next morning; however, of that I was confident. At least for that night, I experienced a glimpse of the joy I had felt in the past.

Chapter Sixteen
No Justice for Children

I Discover the Truth

I was willing to accept Quin's death as something beyond anyone's control. The doctors explained that some things are unforeseen and can't be prevented.

That would have been the easiest path, but a few days after Quin died, I called Dr. Sterling from the medical examiner's office. She did a full autopsy because she felt that a healthy teenager normally shouldn't die from a routine appendectomy.

"Why did Quin die?" I asked.

When she responded, I almost dropped the phone and began crying. She told me that Quin died of intussusception, the same illness that he was diagnosed with at Scripps Mercy Hospital a week before. I could not believe what I was hearing. The Kaiser medical staff was *handed* the diagnosis and they *ignored* it. In one accidental visit to Scripps, doctors were able to determine the cause of Quin's illness. We were only at Scripps for a few hours! Yet, after nearly *five months,* under the care at Kaiser, all doctors could come up with were an apparent urinary tract infection, possible appendicitis, or that Quin was faking his pain. This was the first indication that something went horribly wrong and that Quin's death was preventable. Anger swelled through my body as my fists clenched and my body started to shake.

Dr. Sterling told me she was 99 percent positive that her findings were accurate, but she wanted to be 100 percent sure. She told me that she was going to have a pediatric pathologist from Rady Children's Hospital review her work, because she knew what was coming. I did not ask her what she meant, but I could only assume she knew a lawsuit was coming and that she wanted to make sure all her work was done correctly, without a doubt.

I still had many unanswered questions. I asked Dr. Sterling about Quin's intestines and whether or not they were backed up with feces as Dr. Koglin had indicated a few days before Quin died. Dr. Sterling told me Quin's intestines were *clear*. I also asked about the Meckel's Diverticulum that Dr. Gerund mentioned after Quin's surgery. She told me that she did not see a Meckel's Diverticulum while performing the autopsy. These responses got my head spinning. Everything the doctors told me about Quin when he was suffering was completely wrong.

Dr. Sterling ended the conversation with more disturbing news. She told me that two Kaiser doctors had contacted her and asked if Quin had been using drugs prior to his death, and if so, if it could have been a factor in his passing. Dr. Sterling seemed highly troubled by their line of questioning, "I thought you should know, Brian," she said.

The doctors called the medical examiner for one purpose only — to determine whether Quin was using drugs. They were not curious or open to another explanation, nor did they entertain the increasingly clear possibility that they made *many* mistakes. Instead of compassion and self-reflection, they desperately wanted to fault Quin.

This news put me in fight mode. I was not going to stop until I knew the truth. I wasn't going to go away.

The MICRA Law: No Justice for Children

While I could not get Quin back, I knew there were things I deserved to know, like the exact reasons that lead to Quin's death, and whether mistakes were made. I wanted Kaiser to apologize for their mistakes and show some compassion for my situation. I wanted them to tell me they took this case seriously, reflect upon it, and implement system-wide changes to address the failures of their medical staff. But that was not to be; their policy instead was secrecy. If they only knew that I didn't care about a financial settlement, and that all I wanted was an authentic, sincere apology, things may have gone differently.

I didn't realize how common my experience was until later. I listened to a podcast with Frank Federico, the Vice President of The Institute for Healthcare Improvement (IHI), who discussed the culture of secrecy among health institutions due to a fear of lawsuits. He said a solution to this culture of secrecy is a model of "Respectful Crisis Management." In this model, when mistakes are made, open communication with patients is supported to discuss any mistakes that may have occurred. The conversation is followed by an apology and just compensation. Federico believes that, "Most families don't sue because they want to become millionaires. They sue because they need the information and are angry at the healthcare system."

Federico is of the opinion that if the hospital made a mistake, it is important to make it right for the patient. Studies at the University of Michigan concluded that open disclosure has dramatically reduced the number of malpractice claims. The University of Michigan Health System devised a model as well. They have a policy of apologizing, having an open discussion, providing full disclosure, and learning from their experiences when a medical error occurs. By "doing the right thing" they have reduced the number of malpractice claims, and legal costs are down by more than 50 percent.

This was not the case for me. I was facing a wall of silence with a standard response, "Sometimes bad things happen, and they can't be prevented."

I could not accept this, because I was being denied validation for the harm that was done. Dr. Gerald Monk, a professor at San Diego State University who specializes in dealing with the aftermath of patient harm, states,

> The healthcare environment is still dominated by the culture of 'deny and defend.' Most physicians have been trained not to apologize when things go wrong and warned by their mentors that it can lead to a lawsuit. Actually, the opposite is true. Harmed patients who do not receive an apology and an open and transparent investigation about what went wrong are often left with a strong desire for justice.

This is exactly what happened to me. Facing this wall of silence and no validation for the harm that was done made me furious. I wanted redemption. I decided I would contact the top law firms in San Diego. I had no doubt in my mind that any lawyer would be eager to take the case, but I was wrong.

To my disbelief, each law firm I contacted was sorry for my loss and sympathetic to my grief, but said they were unable to take on my case. I could not understand why they would refuse a case like mine. Their rote responses frustrated me deeply, because I believed I had a strong case.

I called a childhood friend, Jorge, who was a lawyer in Long Beach. I knew he could shed some light on the matter and help me to understand the lack of legal help I was facing. He had one word for me, "MICRA."

"What is that?" I asked him.

He said, "The Medical Injury Compensation Reform Act (MICRA). This law puts a cap on pain and suffering of a loved one at $250,000. The limit is based on non-economic damages. There is no justice for children who die from medical malpractice due to their lack of wage earning. These cases are incredibly expensive to litigate with little or no incentive. Even if someone is lucky enough to contract a lawyer, in the end most of the money is consumed by the costs."

I was floored by his words. "It just doesn't make any sense," I told him.

"I'm sorry, Brian," he said. "But this is the reality, and I'm pretty sure that is why the law firms you contacted refused to take on your case. Most of the top medical malpractice law firms will only take cases that involve economic damages on top of the $250,000."

"So, because a child doesn't have a job, there are no economic damages a lawyer can sue for?" I asked.

Jorge responded, "You are absolutely right, Brian. I have heard of families of children who have died due to medical malpractice and suing, but after 16 months of litigation and winning, they walk away with very little, because most of the money is eaten up by expenses to try the case. There is no justice for children."

In 1975, the MICRA law was signed into law in California, in response to a perceived, but later discredited, crisis in the rising cost of premiums for malpractice insurance. Even after MICRA took effect, premiums continued to rise. It was only after the passage of Proposition 103 in 1988 that gave the state the power to regulate premium increases, and gave healthcare providers the assurance that they would not be gouged by malpractice insurers. The $250,000 MICRA law limitation has remained unchanged since 1975, despite decades of inflation. It has done little to help doctors and nothing to improve patient care. Its main beneficiaries have been insurance companies.

I later found proof that my friend was right. I came across a study by Joanna Shepherd, Ph.D, Associate Professor of Law and Economics at Emory University School of Law. The study, *Justice in Crisis*, provided an objective analysis on how non-economic caps like MICRA result in the denial of due process for victims. In survey results, she found, "Most attorneys will not accept a slam dunk case, (95% likelihood of winning) unless the expected damages are over $250,000..."

The study found that the majority of attorneys rejected over 90 percent of the cases they screen, and the most common reason for rejecting cases was insufficient damages. This impacts patient's access to justice. She found that, "...attorneys lament that they have no choice but to turn down legitimate cases after their state's enact tort reform." In other words, there is a high likelihood that legitimate claims will go unrepresented. As one attorney she interviewed stated, "I would hate to be a plaintiff out there looking for a lawyer right now."

A Civil Action: "A Dead Child is Worth Least of All..."

The MICRA law has technicalities that are boring to most people. The average citizen does not feel affected by the technicalities, so laws like this continue to exist. There is one scene in a movie; however, that brings the injustice of the MICRA law to life. *A Civil Action*, with John Travolta, begins with Travolta pushing a client in a wheelchair into a courtroom as he narrates the opening lines of the movie:

It's like this. A dead plaintiff is rarely worth as much as a living, severely-maimed plaintiff. However, if it's a long slow agonizing death, as opposed to a quick drowning or a car wreck, the value can rise considerably. A dead adult in his 20s in generally worth less than one who is middle-aged. A dead woman less than a dead man. A single adult less than one who's married. Black less than white. Poor less than rich. The perfect victim is a white male professional, 40 years old, at the height of his earning power, struck down in his prime. And the most imperfect? *Well, in the calculus of personal injury law, a dead child is worth the least of all.*

Now it all made sense why all the top law firms did not want to take my case. I could not believe that the death of a child could be worth less than the life of anyone else. As a society, are we not supposed to protect the lives of innocent children more? How can we as a society put such little value on the lives of our children?

I understand the argument about frivolous lawsuits, but the courts have rules in place to deal with meritless claims. Imagine trying to rationalize with grieving parents that their child's life is worth less because their child died in a hospital, instead of some other random setting.

Justice is not served by limiting the damages of giant corporations. According to Becker's Hospital CFO Report, Kaiser Permanente's operating income grew as membership boomed, and in 2016, their operating revenue climbed to $64.6 billion, while they reported a net income of $3.1 billion.

A grieving parent with no support from the courts is no match for a profitable corporation like Kaiser. A multi-year battle in court means that most of the winnings go to litigation costs and lawyer fees.

A perfect example of how the MICRA law works is the story

of Mychelle Williams and her mother Dawnelle King. Mychelle was 18 months old when she became very sick with vomiting, difficulty breathing, and a fever reaching 106 degrees. She was so ill, the paramedics took her to the nearest hospital near her home in Los Angeles, California, instead of Kaiser. The doctor suspected a massive bacterial infection that could be treated with antibiotics. Before he could do a blood culture, Kaiser convinced them to transfer her. By the time she reached Kaiser, she was near death; she died 20 minutes later. A jury awarded Mychelle's mother $1,353,000. However, in accordance with the MICRA law, the court reduced the verdict to $250,000 for non-economic damages. After appeals and seven years of litigation, the MICRA law won out. A ruling like this sends the message to HMOs that they are shielded no matter how egregious the case, as long as the patient is a child.

Dr. Shepherd's study confirms that children are silent victims, along with low-income groups, women, the elderly, and minorities. The most vulnerable among us do not have the same access to due process, and there is little they can do to receive justice.

The Josie King Story

This was the reality I faced. At this point, I should have given up. But I had heard of another story that gave me hope. It was the story of a child, Josie King, who died due to medical errors at one of the most renowned medical institutions in the world, Johns Hopkins. Josie's mother, Sorrel, turned her grief into a campaign to eliminate medical mistakes. She found the most extraordinary partner in Dr. Peter J. Pronovost, a patient safety expert and physician at Johns Hopkins. Their goal was to transform the culture of America's hospitals by listening and working together with patients in order to build better technologies and a system that prevents medical errors.

Sorrel King says "Families who have lost loved ones to medical mistakes want hospitals to do three things in the aftermath: Apologize; tell the truth; and take steps to fix the problem."

It was as if Josie's mother was reading my mind. I wanted Quin back more than anything, but if I couldn't have that, I wanted those three things from the hospital. If Johns Hopkins could do all three, maybe Kaiser could do the same for me.

I never received an apology. Perhaps they thought that saying "I'm sorry" would be tantamount to admitting guilt. I, unlike Sorrel King, found no equivalent to Dr. Peter Provonost; someone who would listen to patients, and together help prevent similar mistakes. Kaiser was not Johns Hopkins, and I felt powerless.

Chapter Seventeen
Not Giving Up

My chances of getting a reputable law firm to take my case seemed to be out of reach. I wanted justice for Quin, but the MICRA law was a roadblock. Some people might have given up after the rejection of five law firms. But I didn't care, even if I had to fight the case myself, I had to find out the truth.

I received a phone call from my dad, who told me that he had spoken to his good friend, JD, who wanted to help us. JD was retired from law enforcement and also an entrepreneur. He wanted to meet with Ticia and me. Ticia was at the hospital every day when Quin was sick. She was also my dad's best female karate student. At tournaments, she often fought against the boys, and won. She was everyone's protector, just like my dad. My dad was a black belt and ran his own karate studio. He, like my sister, stood up to injustice.

When I was 10 years old, my dad took me and my twin brother to an amusement park. As we stood in a long line for a ride, I witnessed my dad for the man I always knew he was. Two big men in their early 30s stood in front of us. They cursed loudly and dominated their territory with a wide stance. In front of them stood an older couple. One of the men took out his lighter and lit it under the older man's back side, while his friend laughed.

The older man turned around and yelled out, "Hey! What are you doing?"

Then they pounced. They both leaned into him and yelled back at the old man, "What are you going to do about it?"

That is when my dad stepped in. My dad yelled out in his loudest voice, "Leave him alone!"

They both turned immediately and started to come toward my dad.

I saw my dad's facial expression and posture turn into that of a warrior, with a karate stance. It was natural to him. He had practiced this hundreds of times, but now he needed it for real. He said, "Let's go, right now, you…!" He used the language they would understand, although I had never heard him talk that way before. He never cursed in front of us, so I knew he was serious.

As soon as these bullies saw that my dad was not going to back down, their inflated posture began to shrink. It was like a balloon had been popped. They put their heads down, turned around, and didn't say another word.

Not long after, security came and took them away in handcuffs. The entire crowd in line cheered.

This was a defining moment for me. This is how the Murphy's reacted to injustice. We were not going to be afraid of bullies. My sister, a superb athlete and strong woman, embodied my dad's example more than anyone I knew.

Ticia was at the hospital everyday advocating for Quin. Quin's death was a shock to everyone, but she took it especially hard. She felt responsible, and the fact that she couldn't save him was killing her. So she was part of that meeting. My dad, Ticia, and I agreed to meet with JD.

JD gave me a big hug. We gathered around the table. JD told us he had experience dealing with lawyers through law enforcement and his business dealings. He told us that the first thing we needed to do was to get a copy of Quin's medical records. The medical records would help write a detailed timeline of events from beginning to end. We would summarize Quin's entire medical treatment at Kaiser that led to his death.

JD said it wasn't going to be easy, and that it would probably take us months and hundreds of hours to complete. I wondered why it would it take so long to write. I had no idea what I was walking into.

A week after Quin died, we started to collaborate and split up the massive amount of work ahead of us. Bo, had the task of getting the medical records. She wanted to do everything she could to help. She wanted justice for our son as well.

She arrived at Kaiser's office of Patient Access and requested a copy of Quin's entire medical history. At first, the women behind the desk was happy to help, but then she entered Quin's name into the computer. She had a puzzled look on her face. She said she was unable to access Quin's records. His records were locked. Bo was determined. She had a right to her son's medical records and wasn't leaving without them. The attendant began to get flustered and tried to make excuses. After a two-hour wait, Bo finally got the records. She immediately gave them to me, so I could start on the timeline.

When I saw Quin's medical record, I understood why it was going to take us so long to make sense of them; the record was 800 pages. We would have to analyze every page and compare it with our account of what happened. I took the record to my sister, Maria's, house. We spread the pages out on the dining room table and divided them into different stacks. When that table was completely full, we added two large folding tables.

Our goal was to read each entry and create a timeline of events. We were going to find out what went wrong. We were on a mission to find out the truth.

I was determined to do the best possible job I could; nothing was going to get in my way of justice for Quin. Every waking free moment I had was spent either researching Quin's medical records or writing the account of what happened. Family and friends helped read, interpret, and write. Maria helped me with the writing of the timeline, and my brother-in-law, John, was our technical expert, linking the summary to the medical records. We would sit for hours on the computer making sure to account for every detail. Our friend, Sherri, spent days reading the records and interpreting them to help us understand the meaning of the medical language.

We had assembled our own research team, doing the work a prestigious law firm would do. We spent every free moment compiling a case for Quin. In the end, it took approximately 300 hours of work to complete the 40-page timeline, linking all the events to Quin's medical records.

JD collected all the work we had completed and created a professional-looking document to present to different law firms. Every hospital visit and encounter with a Kaiser's medical staff was documented in the timeline and linked to the medical notes. JD also created CD copies, and delivered our final product to a few different law firms that specialized in medical malpractice cases.

Although we were told that no law firm would take our case, I could not allow myself to sit passively. When harm is done, there is a need to take strong action. Otherwise, the harm will be repeated over and over again.

I was in the midst of the worst moments in my life. My son had just died, but I couldn't help but think of that moment when my dad taught me to stand up and fight. I wasn't fighting two bullies in an amusement park line, I was fighting one of the largest, wealthiest medical companies in the world. To me, I was simply fighting for Quin. I was fighting for the truth.

Chapter Eighteen
A Good Omen

It had been two months since Quin's death. This time we were more prepared to convince a law firm to take our case. We had compiled a massive document that included a detailed summary with links to the medical records. We noted every medical mistake that lead to Quin's death. The cover sheet was a photo of a healthy Quin playing soccer. This was our one shot. We did all the research. We had all the proof.

The first time I contacted law firms, they all rejected me. This time, the response was different. We received several phone calls, but the first phone call came from a prominent malpractice law firm. They wanted to meet with us right away. Just having a firm acknowledge us seemed like winning the first of many battles. What changed?

The personal secretary for one of the law partners called. She had read the story and was moved to tears. She saw the pictures of Quin and our family, and immediately gave it to the head lawyer. "You have to read this," she said.

It was St. Patrick's Day. Normally, he would not have taken a second glance, but something compelled him to open it. It was rare for a client to do all the research and compile the evidence ahead of time. However, there was something else that drew him in. He saw the name on the cover and curiously turned to the first page. Once he started reading, he could not stop. He realized that this might be the case they were looking for.

The day arrived to meet with the lawyers. JD, Bo, Ticia, and I met in the lobby. As we took the elevator up, we made light conversation to break up the intensity in the small space. I don't remember what we talked about because my thoughts were somewhere else. I replayed the typical law firm response in my head, "Sorry for your loss, but we can't take your case at this time."

We walked into the law firm's office. I looked all around to see they occupied the entire top floor of the building. A receptionist escorted us to a spacious room with a large table in the center. "Would anyone like coffee or water while you wait?" she asked.

I had a feeling they were trying to impress us, and it was working. A gentleman walked in and introduced himself as one of the partners of the law firm. He was extremely energetic and happy to see us. "Hi, my name is Quin, thank you for coming," he said.

I couldn't process what he just said. *Did he just say his name was Quin?* He saw the shocked looks on our faces and tried to explain, "I received your information on St. Patrick's Day, and when I saw your son's name on the document, I almost fell out of my seat. It must be a good omen."

Already, we had so much in common; Irish ancestry and a name. He impressed me from the very beginning. He personified strength and confidence. He told us he was outraged by Kaiser's treatment of Quin. He believed that Kaiser was so negligent in mishandling Quin's care, that they would do everything possible to circumvent the MICRA law, taking the $250,000 cap off the table.

He broke down the strategy for us. He would use civil law code 3428, which was based on failure to provide services or the denial of health care to a patient. Quin was *denied* the care he needed when the GI specialist refused to come to his bedside and treat him, ultimately leading to his death. He said the law firm had been waiting for a case like this, and he believed this would be the case to get around the MICRA law, the law that prevents justice for those harmed by medical errors.

He went on to say that he was going to use legal maneuvering to avoid Kaiser's mandatory arbitration and get Quin's case into Superior Court. If he could prevail by using this law code, then the MICRA's $250,000 cap could be bypassed. Consequently, Kaiser could be sued for the true damages that the MICRA law unfairly denied.

Most people are not aware that when you sign up for a popular HMO like Kaiser, you unknowingly sign a contract that takes away your constitutional due process rights to receive a trial by jury. Enrollees must instead resolve any dispute through arbitration. Arbitration proceedings are more secretive than trials, thus, preventing other enrollees from learning about systematic failures or incompetent doctors. Decisions are not reported, and are not binding in future cases, so the same issues may be arbitrated again and again. On the other hand, if it goes to court, the party at fault must refrain from specific acts, thus, preventing the same mistakes from repeating. Unfortunately, most patients do not know this information until they are harmed by medical malpractice, and by that time it is too late.

In the *New York Times* article, "For Patients, Unpleasant Surprises in Arbitration," the author states that an increasing number of healthcare providers are pushing for binding arbitration to reduce their costs. There are negative consequences to this trend.

Critics say one troubling aspect of arbitration is its secrecy. Proceedings are often confidential. There is no public airing of issues or acknowledgment of error, and no development of case law or establishment of precedent. 'Part of the value of the Seventh Amendment right to a trial by jury is the public sees the facts,' said Jamie Court, executive director of the Foundation of Taxpayer and Consumer Rights."

As I listened to this lawyer enthusiastically explain how he would bypass arbitration, I cautiously allowed myself to feel hope. I allowed myself to believe that I could receive everything I asked for. I wanted Kaiser to explain why Quin's pediatrician delayed a referral to a specialist, how they could dismiss so many symptoms and red flags, and why the GI specialist refused to see Quin and instead said he needed a psychiatrist. I wanted them to understand how much pain they caused me and say, "We are sorry." I wanted corrections made in their system. I wanted the whole story to be told so that these failures could not be hidden by the protection of arbitration. All of these thoughts were going through my head during the meeting.

The meeting lasted about an hour. Before we ended, I had one last concern to discuss with the lawyer. I had been warned that most people sign non-disclosure agreements once a case is settled. Doing so would prevent me from speaking about the case. I told the lawyers that under no circumstances would I sign a non-disclosure agreement that would prevent me from telling Quin's story.

"Kaiser took my son, but they won't silence me," I told him.

"We won't allow that to happen, Brian," he replied.

We had nothing to compare our meeting to, but our friend, JD, who had many encounters with lawyers said, "You guys just received the Cadillac treatment from this law firm. This rarely happens. You should consider yourselves lucky. It is up to you, but I don't think you will get a much better offer than what you received today."

We were convinced that we had found our law firm. The next day, JD called the lawyer and told him we wanted them to represent us, and that some of the family would like to meet him. The lawyer was happy about our decision and said that he would love to meet the entire family.

Twenty-two family members came to the meeting. The team of lawyers were there to greet us. They looked at my identical twin brother, Conan, and their eyes locked on him, greeting him with enthusiasm. They thought they were greeting me. This happens to us often. I walked in behind my twin, and the lawyers looked confused, looking from Conan's face to mine, trying to figure out who was who. It was a brief moment of humor.

The lead lawyer looked impressed by how many family members showed up, and said that he had never experienced anything like it in his 30 years of practicing law. He commented that we had done a lot of work, but now it was our time to rest, and they would fight for us now.

Our new team fighting for Quin seemed to also think that our encounter was fate. The coincidences were too many; our lawyer's name was Quin, and they received the case on St. Patrick's Day. The paralegal was also an identical twin whose maiden name was Murphy. Maybe it was a coincidence, or maybe just a sign that we found the right firm.

Before I handed them the signed contract, I wanted to make sure one last time they understood I would not sign a confidentiality agreement that would prevent me from telling Quin's story.

"You have nothing to worry about," said the lawyer.

Chapter Nineteen
The Lawsuit

Our first battle was won; we found a law firm that would accept the case. Even though I fought tirelessly to get to this point, handing over control was difficult. Working on the case myself gave me a purpose. Now, I could only wait for the occasional update from our lawyers. I constantly checked my emails and voice messages, anticipating any news.

I continued to spend hours researching. I would read Quin's records repeatedly and research Kaiser's history, as well as cases similar to Quin's. I tried not to bother the firm, but I emailed them weekly to ask for updates. I asked if they had a medical expert witness review Quin's CT scans. They said that a pediatric GI agreed with them that Kaiser was negligent in Quin's care.

"Yes, we've consulted with a gastro who has confirmed the original and appropriate diagnosis of intussusception by Scripps, and Kaiser missed it. This is a straightforward breach of the standard of care," they replied.

One year would pass before a court date was set to argue whether or not Quin's case would remain in Superior Court. It happened to fall on the day before Quin's birthday, June 2, 2011. I kept my phone in my hand all day long. My lawyer had told me earlier that if the judge denied our claim, all would be over. Kaiser lawyers were arguing that there was no legal basis for our claim in Superior Court and asked the judge to dismiss our case.

At 3:00 p.m. on June 2, I got the call. My lawyer gave me the details as they unfolded in court. At first, the judge denied the claim, but the lawyer said they weren't going to go down without a fight. The lawyer explained how he argued fiercely and told the judge they had undeniable proof that Kaiser denied the treatment Quin needed.

"Scripps gave a correct diagnosis of intussusception. Kaiser ignored the diagnoses and wrote in the records that it was in his head. Then he died of intussusception," they argued.

The judge listened and determined that the evidence was there to allow the case move forward. The lawyer noted that as they walked out of the courtroom, they noticed the expression on the face of the lawyer who represented Kaiser. He was wide-eyed and visibly shaken, as if not used to losing. Normally, a lone patient, even with proof, has no chance against the power wielded by teams of well-funded Kaiser lawyers.

In the end my lawyer said, "We won, Brian! Today was a good day for Quin."

My lawyer explained the next step. "This was a big win for us, but now comes the discovery of evidence to prove Kaiser doctors negligently delayed and denied Quin's health care." He told me that he would begin deposing doctors and acquire evidence to build a case for trial. He explained that it would not be easy. After Kaiser lost the first battle, they hired a big law firm out of San Francisco that specializes in managed healthcare issues. We had gotten their attention. Normally, they take it for granted that cases brought against them will be thrown out of court and back into arbitration. Kaiser enjoyed the comforts of arbitration, where they could control negative exposure. With Quin's case in Superior Court, they could be exposed to bad publicity. All I cared about was getting my day in court. Kaiser doctors would have to answer all the questions I had. I wanted to understand why they refused to help Quin, and why they believed he was faking his illness.

It was great to receive such good news the day before Quin's birthday. For me, it was another sign—one of many—that I received throughout this ordeal. There were times when I felt like giving up, but then I would receive a sign that would help me feel connected to Quin. I know it was superstitious to think Quin was trying to communicate with me, but this is what kept me going at the time.

Many of the signs I received came unexpectedly; like the time I went into Quin's room after he died, and I found a book on his nightstand. He was reading a book on naval history and the Spanish-American War, the war in which my great-grandfather won the Congressional Medal of Honor. It prompted me to read about the mission, and I found this quote about my great-grandfather, "...displayed extraordinary heroism... sinking of the U.S.S. Merrimac, Santiago de Cuba, June 3, 1898."

Also, on Quin's birthday! Maybe Quin's birthday was a lucky day. Everything was falling into place and meant to be. I couldn't wait to tell everyone the great news, Quin's case was moving on to Superior Court.

The judge allowed the case to go to Superior Court, but now came the hard work of proving the negligence, and that would take money. Our firm was hoping to force Kaiser to release their business practice documents. If the records showed that Kaiser's practice was to save money, even if that meant delaying and denying what a patient needed, that would prove that Kaiser's failures were systemic in nature.

Lawyers had been trying to get these records for years, but Kaiser protects their secrecy at all cost. My lawyers requested the records in discovery and when Kaiser refused, our lawyers filed a motion to compel their production (release their records). Unfortunately, my lawyers were not able to convince the trial judge to force Kaiser to release the records.

A few months passed, and each time I asked my lawyers when we were going to do depositions on Kaiser doctors, they would tell me that depositions would be rescheduled or coming soon. My intuition was telling me something was wrong.

Looking back, I believe it was at this point that our lawyers gave up. Instead of filing an appeal regarding the judge's decision not to compel Kaiser to release their records, scheduled depositions of Kaiser doctors were suddenly canceled. I was frustrated because I wanted so badly to know why my son died. Instead, Kaiser lawyers scheduled depositions to be done on us. Our depositions were not canceled. Kaiser wanted to know exactly what we knew. At the same time, our lawyers were doing nothing to try to ascertain why Kaiser failed to provide Quin medical attention, or to further compel Kaiser to produce their records.

My deposition was first and it was one of the most difficult, emotional things I have ever done. It was almost two full days of Kaiser's lawyers asking me questions about every detail leading up to Quin's death. It felt like I was reliving every horrific detail all over again, and the lawyer was like a robot with no emotions. I was recounting the most traumatic moments of my life to a lawyer who was trying to gather evidence to prove their client was innocent. I felt so much anger as they tried to twist and turn my words, implying that the doctors did nothing wrong.

Near the end of my deposition, I described the last moments of Quin's last breath, as I held him looking into his eyes. I explained how I yelled at the doctor to please help. My voice cracked and tears fell from my eyes. At this moment, I looked up at the lawyer and saw a glimpse of a human being. He was shaking his head and in a sympathetic tone said, "I'm sorry for your loss." I saw a crack in the robot's heart. There was a real human under there, perhaps a father with empathy. I felt for a moment that he was genuinely sad for my loss.

Bo and Ticia had their depositions next, and it was a repetition of the same grueling questions. He wanted to know who was there, what they said, and what they heard. Listening to Bo's sobs of pain felt like being stabbed in the chest. I couldn't protect her or my sister from this unbearable pain.

Ticia was a warrior and a protector, and she could not accept her failure in saving her nephew. She described the effect Quin's death had on her. Even when things appeared normal to the outside observer, inside she felt like screaming at the top of her lungs. She couldn't. She just held it in and it was killing her. She had to act appropriately and polite, but inside there was a caged animal that wanted to lash out.

It was four days of depositions and we were all glad when it was over. Now, it was our turn to depose the doctors. I kept having a nagging feeling again that something was wrong. A few weeks went by and still there were no depositions scheduled. My lawyer finally emailed me and said he would like me, Bo, and Ticia to come into the office for a meeting to plan our strategy going forward. While this news made me nervous, I tried to stay positive.

As we waited in the office for our lawyers to come in, I felt my stomach tighten up. The group of lawyers walked in and wasted no time.

The head lawyer said, "I'm sorry to inform you that we had our medical expert witness review Quin's records and believes it was a surgical error that was the cause of Quin's death. Therefore, we will be notifying Kaiser on a settlement."

I couldn't believe what I was hearing. It took me a minute to process what I had heard. It felt like another punch in the stomach, but this time it was coming from my own lawyers. Because I was unclear, I asked a few questions.

"What do you mean it was a surgical error? The medical examiner clearly said the cause of the death was intussusception."

This was significant, because if the cause of death was a medical error, the damages would be capped at the $250,000 MICRA limitation. We were trying to argue that because Quin died of intussusception, which was treatable by a GI, and Kaiser denied him access to a GI, the cause of death was "delay or denial" of necessary medical treatment, which could take the case outside the MICRA limitations.

One of the lawyers had his head down, and the lawyer leading the meeting replied curtly, "We feel confident that our expert witness is correct in his findings and we will not be able to take the case any further. We are done."

What was he saying? A medical error would be covered under the MICRA law meaning there is a cap of $250,000 even if it's gross negligence. However, I knew that Quin was diagnosed with intussusception and that is what caused his death. Kaiser delayed and denied care, and that is what our case was all about.

"How can your expert witness change the cause of death?" I asked.

"Our expert witness is not changing the official cause of death determined by the medical examiner, but we do not have faith in her finding in a court of law," he said. He was trying to discredit the medical examiner by saying she was not a credible witness.

I walked out of the meeting confused and in shock. Something did not feel right, so I immediately called my friend, Jorge. I told him about the meeting and that our lawyers wanted to settle the case.

Jorge was very surprised and said, "The outcome of a case almost always becomes clear as it moves forward, but in your case it is the complete opposite." Our case seemed very clear at the beginning, but all of a sudden it was vague and undetermined. He agreed that the news our lawyers gave us did not seem right and that we should talk to independent experts to figure out the truth.

Chapter Twenty
My Search for the Truth

After the meeting with the lawyers, my first action was to email them, and tell them to hold off on the settlement so our family could process the news. I was on a mission. When Quin was sick, doctors told me my intuition was wrong. I saw the truth in front of me. My son was literally dying before my eyes, yet, the doctors made me feel like I was overreacting. Now, almost two years later, it was happening again. After getting the correct cause of death from the medical examiner, my lawyers were telling me that Quin died of something else, and we had no case. This time, I was not going to make the same mistake. I was going to find out the truth.

I called the coroner's office. They told me that Dr. Sterling had been promoted to Chief Medical Examiner in another state. I had to find her. I tracked her down on the other side of the country. I didn't know if she would remember our case.

"Hi, Dr. Sterling, I don't know if you remember me. I'm Brian Murphy, and my son was Quin Murphy," I said.

She replied immediately, "Oh yes, I remember your case very well."

I told her that my lawyer's medical expert changed Quin's cause of death from intussusception to a surgical error. She seemed dumbfounded. She said that their explanation was so implausible that it didn't even make sense to her. She said that she even had a forensic pathologist review her work, because she expected the case to be controversial. She confirmed that my intuition was correct, but I needed more evidence.

A good friend of mine was related to a GI who agreed to help. I sent him Quin's medical records, along with the autopsy report and what my lawyer's medical expert witness had determined. After a week, he called me back with his opinion. "I analyzed the records along with a colleague. There is no evidence to conclude that what your lawyers are telling you is correct. I am having a difficult time believing your lawyers are being truthful with you. Are you sure your lawyers are not in collusion with Kaiser?"

I had no idea what conversations my lawyers had had with Kaiser's lawyers, but now I had a reason to believe I could not trust what they were telling me. My guard was up. My wife, Laurie, owned a residential treatment facility for women with eating disorders. She often worked with a radiologist whom she trusted, and who was also an expert witness on cases. He agreed to look at our case. He spent a week analyzing all of Quin's records and CT scans. He didn't know me at all, but when we finally talked, I felt an instant connection. Instead of the constant gaslighting I had been experiencing, I was now speaking to someone who understood.

He said, "I have a son. After reading what happened to Quin, I was in tears." His voice cracked.

He went on to say that there was absolutely no way that my lawyer's conclusion was correct. He said that the coroner was right and Quin died of intussusception. Then he gave more details that to him were even more shocking. He said the Kaiser radiologist noted that Quin had an intestinal blockage and fluid in his abdomen. For him, either one of these findings would have been a huge red flag and a reason to go back in for emergency surgery. Yet, the Kaiser radiologist barely noted it, and he did not collaborate with the doctors to see if there was any follow-up. The Kaiser doctors seemed to ignore the CT scan results completely.

"Most likely…" he continued, "If you had been at Rady Children's Hospital, the doctors and technicians would have been collaborating to come up with a solution."

Knowing that this nightmare could have been prevented was another twist of the dagger. If only Quin had been transferred to Rady Children's Hospital, where they practice comprehensive care, he could have lived. At Kaiser, it was as if each doctor was working independently. I was constantly reminded of how one small decision could have changed the outcome.

All of this reminded me of a news story I had heard on the radio. A teenage boy was so sick and doctors could not figure out what was wrong with him. He was transferred to the same children's hospital that Quin was denied access to by Kaiser. The outcome for this boy was different. The boy described how a team of doctors surrounded his bed. They asked questions, read reports, and collaborated to find a diagnosis. It saved his life. I heard the boy's animated voice describe his amazing experience and how he felt so cared for. As I drove alone in the car, I fantasized that it was Quin's voice saying those words.

The radiologist's analysis was another step toward my mission to find out the truth. He also told me that he could not comprehend how the GI got away with his diagnosis, "patient suffering from psychosocial element. Will benefit from outpatient psychiatry." The radiologist said that not only was this grossly incorrect, it was also cruel. He ended by telling me, "You need to tell your story. By reading this, it made me a better doctor."

I thanked him and tried to pay him. He shook his head, "I can't take this. After what happened to you, I don't feel right taking your money."

I insisted. "Listen, I appreciate so much what you did. You can put it in your son's college fund. I insist." In return he gave me some medical journals so I could submit my story. He was adamant. "You need to tell your story, Brian."

I interacted with three separate and independent professionals; the medical examiner, a GI, and a radiologist. All three took the time to hear my story. All three were compassionate and wanted to help. All three renewed my faith that most doctors go into this profession to heal and do no harm.

Chapter Twenty-One
I Threaten to Punch My Lawyer in the Face

I finally had all the evidence I needed. I was convinced that my law firm was not telling me the truth. I felt betrayed by members of my own team, and it made me realize that I no longer wanted anything to do with the legal system. I emailed my lawyer and told him about my fact-finding quest, and that evidence proved their explanation of Quin's death was wrong.

I imagined the team of lawyers reading over my email, wondering how on earth I found out the truth and proved them wrong. Their response was perhaps more of what I expected after becoming more cynical.

My lawyer did not admit making up a false cause of death to get me to back off. He simply replied in an email, "Regardless of the cause of death, proving it in court is impossible. We don't want to twist your arm, but we recommend a settlement."

To me, this case meant everything. It meant justice for Quin. It meant reform in a broken system. But for my lawyers, it was just another case that needed to be resolved quickly to protect the bottom line.

Kaiser was offering the maximum under the MICRA law, so my lawyers made a business decision not to go any further with the case. They felt they took the case as far as they could, and they did not want to risk losing Kaiser's offer.

Although I didn't want to settle, I told them to move forward with the settlement under two conditions: their medical expert's opinion was wrong about Quin's cause of death, and I would not sign my rights away preventing me from telling Quin's story. They understood and made arrangements to finalize the settlement.

A week later, the lawyer's office called and said they had bad news. Kaiser was not budging on the terms of the agreement and refused to remove the language regarding confidentiality. This meant that if I signed the agreement, I would not be able to talk about what happened to Quin. My lawyer tried to convince me to sign. He told me I should consider telling Quin's story through my family, but that "Quin's death to the average person is not important or relevant, to the extent there is a story to tell." He was just being blunt, but this was one time I was not going to give in.

I replied. "Quin's story may not be important to the average person, but it's important to me, and no one is going to take it away from me, or put restrictions on what I say."

I was determined and started to get angry. They took my son away, but I would not allow them to take away my right to talk about my son.

I said, "I understand that nothing may ever come of Quin's story, but I will never sign Kaiser's gag order and disgrace his memory."

They asked Bo, Ticia, and me to come into the office for a meeting to debrief before we turned down the settlement.

It was March 2012, and we were back in the office where it all began almost two years earlier. The mood had dramatically changed from one of hope to definite mistrust. We were sitting in the office as the head lawyer stormed in by himself. He sat down and threw the contract across the table. Two years ago, when he thought we might win millions from Kaiser, they treated us like royalty. Not anymore. The circumstances had changed.

His body was tense, his finger was pointing and he started yelling, "I had enough of your head-strong Irish stubbornness, I'm taking off my gloves. We are done taking the case any further and you guys are not leaving this office without signing this settlement!"

I looked over at my sister and she had her fists clenched in anger. Bo looked like she was trying her best to hold it together. I kept my cool and turned to him and said, "From the very beginning you knew and agreed we would not sign a gag order."

He lost control and began yelling again, "I have a lot of pressure to make decisions for this law firm so we don't lose money!"

I could not believe he was trying to bully us into signing. Bo started to cry. I started to get upset and told him he needed to calm down, but that only angered him more. Normally, I am calm and easygoing. There are only a few things that can make me lose my cool. What he said next caused me to explode. I was ready to fight him, and I didn't care about the consequences.

He stood up and said, "There is nothing special about his story - tabloid TV at best!" He continued, "It's all your fault your son is dead! You wanted cheap healthcare, so live with the consequences!"

I literally saw red. I stood up. I reached over the table with my fist in his face and yelled at the top of my lungs, "If you don't shut the fuck up, I'm going to put my fist through your face!"

Bo got up and tried to hold me back. My sister turned to Bo and said, "Don't stop him. Let him."

He clearly underestimated me. I could see the fear in his eyes. He immediately backed down, "Don't threaten me."

I put my finger in his face and said, "You threatened me first saying you were going to take your gloves off."

He sat back down in his chair and apologized. In one minute he transformed from a cocky rooster flapping his wings, to being passive and contrite. It took everything in my power to calm down after his callous words.

He mistook my calmness for weakness. He mistook my tolerance for lack of strength. He challenged my conviction that Quin's life had meaning. It was my story to tell. It was my responsibility to share it. I also knew the same mistakes would be repeated over and over again unless the truth was told. The lion came out in me. I knew that confidentiality agreements were a way to keep secrecy in the system and allow the body toll to mount. I was not going to give in.

The meeting ended and we did not sign the settlement. As we walked out of the office, I saw staff members standing outside the door in shock. Everyone in the whole building must have heard us arguing.

Once again, I needed the counsel of my friend, Jorge, and I immediately called him. I told him what had happened in the meeting and how my lawyer tried to force us to sign the settlement.

"Can they make us sign?" I asked.

He responded, "Absolutely not, you are not going to sign it. This is what you are going to do, Brian. Send them an email that says you cannot in good conscience sign the settlement. Tell him to go back to Kaiser and tell them you will take less money, but with no gag order."

Jorge knew that money was never my priority in suing Kaiser, and that I wanted to make some institutional change to help prevent what happened to Quin to another family. Jorge had been by my side helping me throughout the entire lawsuit. I was fortunate to have friends like Jorge, who were willing to help whenever I needed it.

It reminded me of something Quin once said to me, "Dad, you have some great friends, and I hope to build long-lasting friendships like you have."

It made me feel good inside that Quin had recognized the importance of friendships.

I sent the email as Jorge suggested. I felt confident in my decision, and if I walked away with no money, but had Quin's story to freely tell, then I would be satisfied.

A few days later, one of the lawyers on the case called me. He seemed dismayed as he explained the news.

"Brian, Kaiser has agreed to take out the language of confidentiality. I have never known Kaiser to ever do this. You got what you wanted, Brian."

"I always had Quin's story. I was never going to give it up in exchange for money. I couldn't live with myself if I did," I replied.

This battle with my lawyers reminded me of my dad's karate school. He always paired me with the toughest opponent. During a match we fought all-out, not holding our punches, and often finishing with bloody noses and bruises. And, in the end, we always shook hands. It was a sign of mutual respect, even if for a moment we were fierce adversaries. The battle with my own lawyers felt similar. At the time, I felt betrayed by them. I was angry that they wanted to drop the case. I thought that they would be my advocates to the very end.

However, as time passed my anger subsided. After reading about our medical liability system and how it works, I realized that it was a small miracle that they even took my case in the first place. No other law firm would touch it, while they took a big financial risk on me. I can look back now with gratitude. The last time I saw them we were nose-to-nose with our gloves off. I left their office without shaking their hands. If I saw them today, I would extend my hand and thank them without hesitation.

One of Quin's favorite books was, *"The Way of the Peaceful Warrior,"* by Dan Millman. We both read the book and watched the movie together. We were intrigued by the warrior athlete, but found a deeper meaning. After reading *Life Lessons for a Modern Peaceful Warrior*, by Jacob Devaney, I learned that compassion can come in the form of a lamb as well as a lion. Being a warrior does not mean you should put down your sword, because you never know when you might need it. However, you can be fearless and compassionate at the same time. You can be both a lion and a lamb. As I read these words I knew this battle had strengthened me. "The strength to face the challenges in our life always reward us with a refinement and evolution of our soul regardless if we win or lose the battle."

Although we did not get everything we wanted, I felt I had won the most important battle. My love for Quin superseded any financial settlement. This was simply another challenge in my journey to find my voice and my purpose. In the end, I would not be bound to a gag order, and I would be free to write Quin's story.

Chapter Twenty-Two
The Quin Murphy Foundation

I was relieved the lawsuit was finally over. It consumed me for two years and had been my obsession. I researched and basically wrote the entire case for the lawyers. I was constantly engrossed in finding the truth. It was a two-year battle for my life, but I finally realized the lawsuit was a momentary distraction from my pain and depression. I had also lost sight of what was important. There were people in my life who needed me: my daughter, Brianna; my wife, Laurie; and my family and friends. There was also The Quin Murphy Foundation. The Foundation, which started almost accidentally, was to become the instrument in which to tell my story, and continue the memory of Quin. It was to become the instrument to redefine my pain.

The week after Quin died, it was Maria's birthday. She was Quin's godmother. Our family has a birthday tradition that on your birthday, our mother cooks your favorite meal. We always gather at my parent's house to celebrate with great food, singing happy birthday, and gift giving. That year, Maria told our mother she wasn't in the mood for a celebration. Everyone was too sad to celebrate. Our mother; however, knew better.

"No. I know we are all sad, but we have to get together as a family. This is how we are going to get through this," she said.

Maria agreed and she had an idea. Before the party, she went to the bank and opened a memorial account in Quin's name. For her birthday, she had one request of the family,

"If you are planning on buying me a gift, please don't. Instead, write a check to The Quin Murphy Memorial Fund so we can give a scholarship in his name. And one other thing, bring a story about Quin to share."

That night was the birth of The Quin Murphy Foundation. We took turns sharing stories about Quin. We took turns saying Quin's name out loud. It reminded me of a tradition our family celebrates, Dia de Muertos or Day of the Dead. It is a celebration with Mexican, Catholic, and Aztec roots. It is believed that the dead only continue to live, if we, the living, remember them.

I felt Quin's presence that evening, as we shared stories that eased our pain. Even for Brianna, it was a cathartic moment. She had been stoic and almost silent since Quin died. I know now she was still in shock. The morning Quin died, she was sleeping peacefully; no one woke her up to go to school. She woke up on her own very late in the morning, after Bo, and her older brother, Chris, returned from the hospital. She sensed something was wrong. Then she heard her mom talking on the phone. Bo was crying, and Brianna tried to make out the words. Bo had been talking to the coroner's office staff who called to get her consent about donating Quin's eyes. That is how Brianna found out her brother was dead. She was only 8 years old. At that moment, Chris came into her room. Quietly sobbing, he sat on the bed next to her and said, "You know how Quin has been sick for a while?" He paused. "He didn't make it."

Brianna grabbed her blanket and threw it over her head. She

didn't say a word.

As we took turns sharing stories about Quin, Brianna talked about how he would take her to the movies every Tuesday. We saw her cry, so we surrounded her with a group hug.

In some ways, I think the loss of Quin was hardest on Brianna. Sibling relationships are supposed to last a lifetime. Although she opened up to us that night, her silence quickly returned regarding her feelings about Quin and his death. I prompted her often and gently to express her feelings, but in return, I would get the same response, "I don't remember anything."

Those words stirred a fear in me that I too would forget Quin. One day in particular, as I was writing this book, I asked Brianna again, "What is a favorite story you have about Quin?"

Her response was the same, but this time I told her I needed her help and wanted to include her recollections in the book. She seemed to take this request more seriously, and paused quietly to search her memory. Suddenly, a huge grin appeared on her face. She began to tell a story in the greatest of detail. These are her words.

"Quin promised me not to tell, but I guess I can tell you now. We were over at my mom's house and Quin called me over to his room. He said, 'Brianna, can you come over here I need to talk to you.' I dropped what I was doing and ran over to see what he wanted, 'Brianna, I need a favor. Can I borrow your scooter?'

"I put my hands on my hips and said, 'Why? What's in it for me?'

"Quin replied, 'Alan and I are going to sneak out for a little while, and we only have one bike, and we need your scooter. We also need you to let us back in the house when we get back. Can you help us out?'

"'OK,' I said, 'but it will cost you. I want you to take me to the movies tomorrow.'

"Quin replied, 'Deal! Make sure you stay awake so you can let us back in, and don't let mom know.'

"My mom was reading a bedtime story to me. I was getting tired, but I knew I had to stay up; Quin was counting on me. Finally, my mom fell asleep. I saw Quin through the window waving his hands to get my attention. I ran over and quietly opened the door.

"'Thanks Brianna. Tomorrow I'm taking you to the movies,' Quin said. He played mad libs with me all night, and the next day he took me to the movies. It was a great day. I remember how excited I was to help Quin, and it was something between us that made me feel important. My big brother needed me, and it made me feel special. I miss Quin so much, Dad."

Since then, we have been able to share memories and smile. In the beginning, it wasn't so easy. When we were sharing stories at Maria's birthday celebration, on that day that The Quin Murphy Foundation came to be, the pain was still very raw for me. Sharing stories helped me see that I wasn't alone in my suffering. My family's pain was apparent, yet, they were doing everything in their power to support me. Giving away a scholarship was my family's way of telling me they cared about me, and that we would never forget Quin.

That night we collected enough birthday money from family members to give away three small scholarships to graduating high school seniors.

Four months after Quin passed away, I walked on stage in front of a packed school auditorium to present the first Quin Murphy Scholarship. Bo, Brianna, Laurie, Chris, and Ticia stood on stage with me. I told myself I was going to be strong. Every time I thought of Quin or talked about him; however, I would get emotional and tear up. As I walked up to the podium, I could hear a loud chatter that echoed off the auditorium walls. I looked out into the crowd and said, "My name is Brian Murphy, and I am presenting the Quin Murphy Scholarship. My 16-year-old son, Quin, passed away four months ago, as I held him in my arms."

As soon as I said that the room was still. I could see the facial expressions of the students in the front row, and I heard a communal gasp. My voice started to crack. I didn't want to cry, but a tear made a path down my face.

After Quin died, I was merely trying to survive, and do everything possible to keep my sanity. The Dalai Lama's book, *The Art of Happiness*, helped me. There was one story the Dalai Lama recounted, and I felt it was written especially for me, on how to deal with suffering from loss.

The story was about a woman who suffered the death of her child. She had heard that the Buddha had medicine to restore her child to life. The Buddha said he knew of such a medicine, but he needed certain ingredients.

"Bring me a handful of mustard seed from a household where no child, spouse, parent, or servant has died," said the Buddha. She began her search in desperation, but was unable to find a home free from the suffering or death. She saw that she was not alone in her grief.

With great compassion the Buddha said, "You thought that you alone had lost a son; the law of death is that among all living creatures there is no permanence." She learned the lesson that no one lives free from suffering and loss. She had not been singled out for this terrible misfortune and was able to take some comfort in that.

This story helped me formulate the words I spoke on stage that day, as I prepared to present the first Quin Murphy Scholarship.

I spoke from my heart, "When we meet real tragedy in life, we can react in one of two ways — either by losing hope and giving up, or by using the tragedy to find our inner strength and do good.

Through my son's scholarship fund, our family hopes to share our compassion, and through compassion, we hope that we can help families, our community, and society."

I will never forget honoring those three students with the Quin Murphy Scholarship that first year. As we walked off the stage, I could hear loud clapping from the crowd. Strangers came up to me and shook my hand, and gave me words of encouragement. It made me feel good to know that people cared about what we were doing.

In the years since, we've received official nonprofit status, and have given over 140 scholarships, some to students who are going into the medical profession. My goal of telling Quin's story and keeping his memory alive was becoming a reality.

Chapter Twenty-Three
Antidote to Hatred: Forgiveness

I could have easily been consumed with anger. I fantasized about inflicting pain on those who I felt were responsible. I replayed over and over how nurses pleaded for Dr. Wren to come see Quin in the last hours of his life, and how he looked annoyed because I insisted. I searched his bio and found out that he practiced martial arts. I wanted to find out where he practiced, and walk into the dojo and challenge him. There was a morbid, yet satisfying fascination with getting retribution.

I was alarmed at the depth of my desire for revenge. It was so taboo. I couldn't share these emotions with anyone. It was not until I read the work of Dr. Gerald Monk, a professor at San Diego State University, who specializes in dealing with the aftermath of patient harm, that I realized it was normal to have these emotions. He states,

> The desire for revenge can be a common reaction among patients who have survived a terrible medical error or for families who have had a loved one die because of a medical mistake. This is compounded when the expected legal punishment falls far short of expectations.

He goes on to say that it is misplaced to ask victims to encourage forgiveness before the victim is ready. Before forgiveness is given, there must be acknowledgment that harm was done.

I made one last-ditch effort and called a Kaiser representative in the hopes that they would recognize what happened. I read on their website that their ombudsman mediator accepts inquiries for dispute resolution, listens impartially, and gathers information. I described what happened and requested the following, "Did my son's death prompt any changes? Did any policies change to prevent this from happening again?"

I wanted to know that Quin's death was not in vain. She was kind and wanted to help, promising me a quick response. Her reply the next day; however, was not what I was hoping for. "We can't help you at this time."

Since I did not receive an apology, perhaps it is fair to say that those responsible didn't deserve forgiveness, but my devotion to Quin and his memory won out. It was either his voice or my own conscience that challenged my anger. I knew there had to be a better way. I poured over the Dalai Lama's book. I marked and highlighted each page. I reread passages that helped me forgive. I learned that when a person's loss becomes destructive, they do not benefit the person who passed away.

The Dalai Lama encourages one to realize that, "If you really love the person, then you must fulfill their wishes with a calm mind."

I had to fight my desire for revenge, and create a positive state of mind that included patience, tolerance, and kindness. This was the antidote to hatred. I chose this path to honor Quin's memory.

The anger I held for Dr. Wren for ignoring Quin began to subside. The anger I had for Dr. Sabata for believing that Quin's pain was in his head began to transform. It wasn't easy. I had every right to be angry. I had every right to seek revenge. The only thing that stopped me was my love for Quin. My love for him helped me see these doctors as human beings in a system that asks too much of them. I began to think about how they felt, and how they also experience suffering when they lose a patient. I discovered that many HMOs follow a policy of secrecy, and doctors are not allowed to openly and authentically communicate with the grieving family. In some settings, doctors are simply not allowed to grieve or show emotion at all, even though humans crave raw empathy. Dr. Pamela Wimble recounts how physicians are cited for unprofessional conduct for crying at work, although grieving is a healthy reaction and humans bond through shared pain. In addition, doctors who are not allowed to process their grief get sick, she claims. Dr. Wimble has personally experienced the loss of colleagues due to suicide.

> Our profession punishes doctors for grieving, and restricts the medical licenses of those seeking mental health care. So rather than process our grief, many doctors turn to alcohol, drugs, and firearms.

I found out that Quin's surgeon, Dr. Gerund, took time off work after Quin passed away. I wondered if he suffered too? Did he wish to apologize, but couldn't?

Dr. Gerald Monk describes a culture of "deny and defend" that leads to doctors suffering from second survivor syndrome. He states:

> ...many doctors and nurses actually want to apologize when things have gone wrong. Many providers went into medicine because they want to be healers and bring good to people's lives. When things go wrong, it can have catastrophic consequences for providers... They are traumatized by causing the patient harm and they are isolated and trapped with secret knowledge about what really happened.

Fortunately, Dr. Monk sees a growing trend and changing culture of the deny and defend system. Large healthcare systems "...are trying to overcome the barriers in the healthcare environment to open, honest disclosure and encourage apologies when things go wrong... These conversations can be restorative for providers, patients and their families."

Although I did not experience this, my hope is that this trend will grow and benefit others. As for me, I found my purpose in helping others. Quin's story has already had a positive impact, and friends have shared with me how they learned to advocate for their loved ones in a dire medical situation. Some professionals, like Dr. Isaac Kohane, are beginning to see the benefits of tapping into the sense of urgency of a parent or spouse when a patient is dangerously ill. Recently, the medical community has witnessed a growing phenomenon of family members who accelerate the quest for treatments to help their loved ones, moving medical research at a faster pace. They become public advocates, scientific leaders, or as in my case, families helping families. Dr. Kohane advises:

> If your doctors have no good solutions, especially if common sense is telling that your situation is uncommon, use your personal network and the power of Internet search engines to find other families with parallel experiences, and do not fear exploring alternatives when the prognosis appears uniformly grim.

Today, I vacillate back and forth between depression and moments of happiness. Sometimes I believe I have finally conquered my grief, only to be blindsided yet again. This happened in 2016, close to Quin's birthday. Despite all the support I had, I could not resist the darkness that consumed me. My wife, Laurie, was so worried, she reached out for support. My childhood friend, Bobby, took me out to lunch. Like everyone else, he had a general idea of what led to Quin's death, but he did not know specific details. Bobby listened intently, and I saw his horrified expression as I ended with my last words, "I laid him back in his bed. I kissed his forehead and said, 'I love you, Quin.'" Bobby's eyes were filled with tears, and he said, "Brian, you have to write this story. People need to know."

He coordinated a plan with my sister, Maria, so she and I began to meet every weekend to write what would become this book. I found this time together incredibly healing. She typed for me while I released every word that yearned to get out. This weekly ritual evolved as friends joined in to help; it became a community project that helped lift the vale of darkness.

This back-and-forth, between joy and sadness, is simply part of my life now. It's a complicated balance between acknowledging suffering and experiencing joy. I admit there are days I want to hide from the world, but it is my purpose to share Quin's story to help others avoid the same tragedy. This process somehow alleviates my burden.

When I started my research, medical errors accounted for over 1,000 deaths per day in the U.S., the equivalent of two jumbo jets crashing every day. My hope is that instead of countless deaths due to medical errors, we arrive to a point where death is not part of a systematic failure. If Kaiser were to return my call today, I would be willing to work with them to make this a reality.

If I had an alternate history, Quin would be in his early 20s. He would be graduating from college, starting his career, and we would play in the same soccer league. I contemplate this as I come to terms with how the natural order for me was disrupted. I know that replaying my painful memories, with the desire to change the past, is futile. I know now that there will be days when I do not want to wake up. I also realize that I have the power to reframe my pain into something good. I realize that by taking this path, I am now open to feeling Quin's love and even seeing messages he sends me.

On his most recent birthday, I visited Fort Rosecrans National Cemetery where my grandfather is buried. It is there where I feel closest to Quin, because of the message Pop sent me. In my mind, Quin is with him. I found an open parking space near a row of gravestones. My heart was aching and I was downcast, but something made me glance up. And there it was, a gravestone with the name, "Quin" and the epitaph underneath read, "Who said I died?" I smiled and imagined Quin speaking those words to me.

The Quin Murphy Foundation is another way that I feel his presence. Many people see our Foundation as a symbol of our loving, supportive family. We are an example of how to respond in the face of tragedy. The reality; however, is that most people will not start a foundation and raise money for scholarships in their loved one's name. Everyone will process their suffering in their own way. I simply had to find a new way to live in a world without Quin, and my suffering was made lighter by serving others. I could now shift the focus to those around me, so that it was no longer entirely about me.

Now, there are many days when I wake up in the morning and feel fortunate to be alive. I can take one more breath. I can use the energy I have left to reflect and grow as a human being.

I now have the opportunity to tell my story in a different way, and to reframe my pain. Maybe you could call it post-traumatic growth. I could continue to live in the sadness, or I could choose to take a different path. Now I can tell a story of hope, resilience, and love.

Quin and Brian looking over the Grand Canyon. Summer 2009.
Our last vacation together.

Bibliography

Allen, Marshall, and Pierce, Olga. "Medical Errors Are No.3 Cause Of U.S. Deaths, Researchers Say." NPR, May 3, 2016.

Alonso-Zaldivar, Ricardo. "$10,345 per person: U.S. health care spending reaches new peak." PBS, July 13, 2016.

Andrews, Michelle. "For Patients, Unpleasant Surprises in Arbitration." *New York Times*, March 16, 2003.

Brewington, Kelly. "Josie's story; a mother turns grief into advocacy." *The Baltimore Sun*, September 21, 2009.

Buettner, Dan. "Lessons For Living Longer From The People Who've Lived The Longest." *Blue Zones*, March 20, 2014.

Cooper, Zack. "What hospitals waste: Why is the nation's healthcare tab sky-high?" *Yale Insights,* February 12, 2016.

Dalai Lama, and Cutler, Howard C. *The Art of Happiness.* Easton Press, 1998. 258.

Devaney, Jacob. "Life Lessons for a Modern Peaceful Warrior." *UPLIFT,* April 6, 2017.

Donal, Maura. "Ruling Limits Damages in Girl's Death at Hospital." *Los Angeles Times*, March 26, 1999.

Drexler, Madeline. "Guns and Suicide, The Hidden Toll." *Harvard Public Health.* Accessed February 15, 2018.

Dubner, Stephen J., "The Demonization of Gluten." *Freakonomics Radio,* October 18, 2017.

Ellison, Ayla. "Kaiser Operating Income Jumps 85% to $672M," *Becker's Hospital Report,* November 11, 2016.

Find Law For Legal Professionals. "California Code, Civil Code - CIV 3428." Description.

Fittro, Kyle J. "Is Dilaudid Stronger than Morphine?" *Chief Teach*, February 2013.

Kohane, Isaac. "Medical Science Should Learn To Tap The Urgency of Families Desperate To Save Loved Ones." *Common Health*, December 8, 2017.

Kushner, Harold S. "When Bad Things Happen to Good People: Suffering is meaningless unless you decide otherwise," *Jewish Learning*, August 2002.

Consumer Attorneys of California. "MICRA." CAOC.org. Accessed February 15, 2018.

Manteiro, Amanda. "What the Crow Symbolizes." *Collective Evolution,* April 24, 2016.

Marcello, Patricia. *The Dalai Lama, A Biography.* Greenwood Press, 2009.

Mayo Clinic. "Broken Heart Syndrome." Symptoms and Causes. Last modified November 5, 2016.

Mayo Clinic. "Inflammatory bowel disease (IBD)." Overview. Last modified November 18, 2017.

Mayo Clinic. "Intussusception." Overview. Last Modified January 6, 2018.

McCann, Erin. "Deaths by medical mistakes hit records." Healthcare IT News, July 18, 2014.

Mercola, Joseph. "What you see in the toilet can give you valuable insights into your health." Mercola.com, February 14, 2013.

Millman, Dan. *The Way of the Peaceful Warrior: A Book That Changes Lives.* H.J. Kramer, 2006.

Niedowski, Erika. "From tragedy, a quest for safer care." *The Baltimore Sun*, December 15, 2003.

O'Bryan, Thomas. *Autoimmune Fix.* Rodale Books, 2016.

Payne, Jacqueline. "Antibody and antigen tests." *Patient.* November 27, 2015.

Pierce, Olga. "When Harm in the Hospital Follows You Home." *ProPublica,* March 21, 2013.

Rabin, Roni C. "15-minute doctor visits take a toll on patient-physician relationships." PBS News Hour. April 21, 2014.

Reed, Sami S. *Dalai Lama: 75 Motivating and Mind Blowing Life Lessons from the Dalai Lama.* Lulu Press, Inc., 2016. ePub.

Seidman, Saul. *Trillion Dollar Scam: Exploding Health Care Fraud.* United States: Universal Publishers, 2008.

Shepherd, Joanna. "Justice in Crisis; Victim Access to the American Medical Liability System." SSRN Electronic Journal, 2012.

"The Michigan Model: The U-M Health System approach to medical errors, near misses and malpractice claims." University of Michigan Medicine. Accessed February 15, 2018.

"To Err is Human: Building a Safer Health System." Institute of Medicine (November 1999).

University of Pittsburgh Medical Center Schools of the Health Sciences. "Stool Analysis." Test Overview. October 9, 2017.

"US Health System Ranks Last Among Eleven Countries on Measures of Access, Equity, Quality, Efficiency, and Healthy Lives." The Commonwealth Fund, June 16, 2014.

Versel, Neil. "About the Johns Hopkins study on medical errors (Podcast)." MedCity News, May 7, 2016.

Wible, Pamela. "Heart-wrenching photo of doctor crying goes viral. Here's why." America's Leading Voice for Ideal Medical Care, March 20, 2015.

Wikipedia. "Gaslighting." Article. Last Modified January 11, 2018.

Wikipedia. "John E. Murphy." Article. Last Modified November 1, 2016.

Williamson, Marianne. *Illuminata: Thoughts, Prayers, Rites of Passage.* Random House, 1994. 109.

Zaillian, Steven. *A CIVIL ACTION.* Buena Vista Pictures, 1998.